Look at me Now

EVOLUTION OF A NORTHERN SOUL

For

Fiona

Happy reading!

Love,

Maya George x

2020

Maya George

© Maya George, 2018

Cover illustration © Helen Stanton, 2018

First published in the UK in 2018

This edition (2019):
Tyne Bridge Publishing, City Library,
Newcastle upon Tyne, United Kingdom
tynebridgepublishing.org.uk

ISBN: 9780950317823

Design & Edit | David Hepworth
Format | Helen Smith

This book is a work of fiction.

For everyone who encouraged me —
you know who you are.

To Lizzie Moffitt, my amazing mum. Enjoy every day of retirement! May your year, and your diary, be filled with happy memories. Lots of love, Sam xxx.

January

Tuesday 8 January

Utterly, totally, and completely failed to muster the energy required to heave my sorry carcass out of the front door for Pilates with the beautiful people tonight. Why anyone in their twenties, or right mind, would consider an exercise class appropriate behaviour for a young person is beyond my comprehension! Shouldn't they be out with their friends, bingeing on the happy hour cocktails? For goodness sake, some of them are students! That lot have absolutely no excuse whatsoever. At least with the twentysomethings there's a slim chance that they have to get up for work the next day. Perhaps they usually go out on the town on Mondays *pretending* they're still students therefore wanting a quieter, healthier time of it on a Tuesday. No, I'm being too generous — they're fundamentally boring and much too thin to drink. Seriously, why would you bother with any form of exercise class at that age? I didn't go anywhere near a gym until I was at least a thirtysomething, after realising that the woman in Spain had turned out to be something of a spiteful soothsayer, cheerily predicting that chocolate would go 'straight to my hips' after I was thirty. How does that work? Do women possess some sort of inner chocolate-channelling system, pre-programmed to 'Hips' at the stroke of midnight on our thirtieth birthday? Maybe 'Thighs' is activated on our thirty-second and 'Stomach' saved for a special thirty-third surprise present.

Put on my PJs extra early tonight in case I shamed myself into going to Pilates after all. If ever there was an exercise discipline hobby/torture/health craze that *didn't* sound like it was named after someone, I would say Pilates was it. Let's suppose it was a multiple choice quiz question (and I didn't already know the answer) about which of the following was named after someone, I can well imagine arguing myself and the whole team out of the rollover jackpot on the grounds that it couldn't possibly be Pilates, because Pilates sounds exactly like some biological process, not a German bloke's surname. So, everyone, it must be Taekwando, which nearly always has a capital letter. Could possibly win a bonus question by knowing that his first name was Joseph. Pilates, not Joseph Taekwando who doesn't, and never did, exist.

Oh yes, almost forgot — man in post office was very animated when serving young woman in front of me but when it was my turn his face slowly dropped and he transformed into some sort of disinterested, glassy-eyed automaton. Should have asked him if he was feeling okay but I bet he would have answered, 'Yes,' in a monotone, thus wasting the irony on him. Instead I apologised for being over fifty, albeit silently. Might look at non-surgical facelifts, again. Oh no, after a week of putting it off, my first diary entry isn't looking too good on the happy memories front — sorry Sam.

Weds 9 January

Did practically nothing. I missed going to the Refugee Centre but they were closed as the boiler was broken, yet again. I would buy them a new one if I had the money. But now I am what's known as a 'pensioner', though not the old-age variety — more like a middle-aged one I suppose. Sounds awful, whichever way it's put. Now I have the time I used to yearn for — too much of it, actually, with not enough money to fill it. Or is it the motivation that's lacking? You can assure your friends that you're enjoying the break and novelty of not being at work for only so long; five months might be taking it to the wire.

Thursday 10 January

Met Sara for coffee at one of those uber-irritatingly trendy places in town (or 'Toon' as we locals call Newcastle) bursting with rotten old tat you're supposed to exclaim, 'Ooh!' at, 'sourced' from those reclaimed furniture places. Whatever happened to the word 'bought'? Why oh why must everything be bloody well 'sourced'? After a very long interrogation, I finally placed an order, feeling relieved I'd been able to answer all the questions without asking, 'What's that?' Why can't it be, 'With or without milk?' for God's sake? And don't get me started on syrup and sprinkles. I haven't got all night. Well, that's not strictly true. I love Sara BUT I always feel extra old meeting her. She's ten years younger than me *and,* to make matters worse, the sun was shining right in my face, not hers, illuminating my 'laughter lines' (ha bloody ha) and making them look more like trenches from the first world war. Should call them the *front* lines.

Lovely Sara, she does make me laugh. I miss that since leaving work. The regular, girlie chit-chat, sniggering in staff meetings like naughty kids, having a good moan about how unbearably noisy the pubs in town are now and how much paperwork or marking we had to do. Sara said I should try internet dating and I replied that my knickers were all grey now at the very moment when she was trying to be ever-so sophisticated, sipping her caramel blah blah latte thing. Suddenly, it came cascading out of her nose, covering the table in a most *un*sophisticated foamy brown mess resembling beach sewage! However, it stopped her from making any more stupid suggestions; karma? Came home and had a look at '2gether.com' — that dating site with a stupid pseudo-trendy name. Did it for a laugh. Definitely not telling Sara.

Friday 11 January

First volunteering day of the New Year at the Centre. Brilliant! A generous couple called in to donate several bagsful of cute miniature samples of what Mum would have described as 'smellies' — although that makes them sound rather foul. They weren't. They were all expensive brands; luxury items that the refugees at the Centre could only dream of being able to afford. I always speed up to a near-jog when passing the glam young things in make-up departments who've trowelled on fifty shades of orange foundation, in case they are offended by the sheer look of horror on my face when they tell me the price of their beauty. I'm afraid of blurting out the truth one day and saying, (exactly like my grandmother) 'Why don't you take all that crap off your face? You are gorgeous!' Except, Gran wouldn't have said 'crap'. More likely to have been 'muck'.

Fortunately, there wasn't a trace of orange muck amongst our lovely samples and we shared out the booty between the families who crowded round excitedly. It was heartening to see the women enjoying the sensation of the luxurious hand cream with its exotic smells — reminders of home, perhaps, and the pleasure on the men's faces as they unearthed a rare gem from the bottom of the bag in the form of a male grooming product. Minika became transfixed, carefully massaging coconut perfumed oil into the parched, flaking skin on her arms, rejuvenating it after the punitive effects of using the cheapest soap she could find. It felt like a lifetime ago since the young Nigerian woman had been able to pamper herself like this; indeed, it was in her previous life. Michael attempted to bring life back to his chafed and neglected hands, worn out from years spent toiling the Eritrean land.

The donors of the treats were real business types: designer gear, flash car and teeth to match. Not your stereotypical refugee fundraisers — whatever they may look like. I love it when people surprise you by not conforming to the pigeonhole that your brain, via your eyes and experience of life, has packaged them neatly into. Their kindness gave everyone a much-needed boost, a diversion from the trauma of the past and uncertainty of the present.

No news of Jakub yet. A new, incredibly polite man came in today asking for the legal team. Typically anxious and looking exhausted, he wasn't interested in the smellies.

Saturday 12 January

Wasted the majority of the day seeeeeething. Not good. Saturdays used to be happydays (does that rhyme?) doing either a million things or nothing at all after the long week at school, but doing it with Sam or with Twat — before he officially became a twat of course. Retirement means that Saturdays no longer hold the same importance, but old habits die hard, and I am an old habit and therefore a Die Hard like Bruce Willis! Twat, on the other hand, is the antithesis of Bruce Willis — in *Die Hard*, that is. I don't know what he's like in real life. He may well also be a twat. Will google it later. Due to his extreme lack of willpower and determination to be a contender for 'The Most Selfish Bastard Who Ever Walked This Earth' award, my ex-husband managed to cause terrible upset to his daughter and condemn me to a sentence of early retirement with not quite enough to do. I HATE HIM!! Oops, pressed too hard with the pen. Have managed to wind myself up into a 'radge' — Sam's favourite Geordie word. It means exactly what you'd expect — think that's onomatopoeia, not sure, will have to google it after Bruce.

Sunday 13 January

A MUCH better day! Out for lunch with Sam. She checked that I was keeping the diary. Didn't dare disclose that it was largely full of moaning and whingeing! I know she thinks the diary will encourage me to do more since retiring in July, but I'm not sure if it won't simply serve as a blow-by-blow account of exactly how tedious my life is and send me spiraling into an even worse decline. What a cheery, uplifting thought. Happy new year to one and all!

Sam is so sweet but can be rather bossy at times. I know she's trying to help but she forgets the age gap and fundamental differences between her single life and mine, given that she's in her early twenties. She keeps banging on about 'getting out there' and 'going for it' and 'making eye contact' with any male who takes my fancy. It's okay for her, she doesn't even need to attempt to make eye contact because men are always trying to get right in her line of sight. Don't know how she manages to see ten feet in front of her with the constant barrage of good looking young (and even more not-so-young) men vying for her attention! Lunch was no exception. Waiter was positively overjoyed when we, correction, *she*, sat down at one of his tables and couldn't have done more to please us; it was useful but don't think I've ever felt so invisible. Sounding like a nasty, jealous, mean mother now. Of course I'm proud of her. I'm her mum! I'm proud of everything she's achieved: her budding career in medical physics, her beautiful personality (entirely down to me of course) and yes, I'm proud of how beautiful she is (cue the *but*) *but*, she doesn't half make me feel ancient!

I remember when I was a teenager on holiday when my parents would take me and a friend out for a meal and Mum would say, 'Ooh yes, we got excellent service today didn't we?' or 'He's very pleased to see you two again!' I had absolutely no idea what she could possibly mean by that.

After all, the waiter was an *old* man who must be nearly thirty years of age, why would he be at all interested in us, two sixteen year old girls? Ah, the joy of naivety. I miss it like a threadbare teddy, taken for granted and a quintessential part of your life for years and years, then someone comes along and throws it in the bin declaring that you're too old for it now — and nothing is the same from that day onwards. I'm remembering *the* incident now — ugh. I feel sick. The friendly, kindly *old* (i.e. anyone over thirty) man sitting opposite me in the empty metro carriage who made polite conversation then masturbated in front of me — a seventeen-year-old girl — while I sat terrified, frozen with fear, looking away. Despite my efforts, his hideous face and the bestial noises he emitted became indelibly etched on my memory.

My naivety lessened that day and I spent many years reliving the moment, angrily daydreaming about what I *ought* to have done and would definitely do if it happened again. I would shout, yell, scream at him, kick him to the ground and stamp on his stupid, grotesque penis *then* press the emergency button. I would be angry, not afraid. But it's far less likely to happen now. Years ago they were referred to as 'flashers', trivialising and downgrading their revolting act of sexual assault to something akin to a harmless hobby. There is nothing harmless about mentally scarring a young person for life. Their victims are carefully selected. Bet I can't get to sleep as yet again feeling radgey after thinking about filthy, perverted men GRR!!

Monday 14 January

Don't search 'is Bruce Willis nice in real life?' if you are a fan. I am choosing to ignore it and sticking with The Boss (or is that the Springsteen Bruce, yes I think it is) BECAUSE I found a quote where BW says in an interview, 'Women should be in charge of everything, women are smarter.' Love you Bruce! I was right about onomatopoeia. Another example is *twat.*

Tuesday 15 January

Someone farted in Pilates. An arty farty Pilate?

Weds 16 January

Thank God for the Refugee Centre! Always feel:
a) useful
b) appreciated
c) not in the least bit invisible
d) like *me*

There was still no news of Jakub. He could already be dead for all we know, or forced back into the youth militia in the Democratic Republic of Congo from which he fled. I can't bear to think about it. How could anyone condemn an intelligent, honest, hardworking young man — *a boy*, to such a fate? If the charity workers who helped him escape could recognise his attributes, how come no one here appreciated how exceptional he is? No one is singled out for help in these places, but he was. Imagine: he risked his life defecting from the youth militia, begged the charity workers to help him flee the country, at great risk to themselves, then arrived in a supposedly civilised country only to be promptly sent back because, in THEIR opinion, it's perfectly safe for him there. How can they sleep at night?

At a time like this I desperately want to believe in God, heaven and therefore, hell because at least I would get the satisfaction of knowing that those responsible would be sent there, after being forced to queue up for hours, of course. Hopefully they would have a detention centre type of place, or exactly the same for that matter, as I've heard that it's hell in there. Feel better after writing about it. Cathartic, this diary writing business.

Thursday 17 January

Met Simon at the Tyneside Cinema. Love it there, it's like stepping back in time, Art Deco time, when everything was — well — Art Deco. Saw one of those French subtitled films where you emerge feeling culturally and intellectually superior to absolutely everyone else around you but mentally drained from having to concentrate and read stuff when you're supposed to be relaxing. You also feel cheated, having paid nine pounds fifty to *not* laugh, not even once. Still, I have to try these things and Simon genuinely likes them. Had a drink in cinema bar, ruined by Simon mentally beating me into submission until I agreed to go to the next speed dating event he could find. I did it with the sole intention of shutting him up oh yes and because he bribed me with a whole solid hour of feet- tickling. WHAT HAVE I DONE?

Friday 18 January

Hell's bells! Simon emailed details of a speed dating night TOMORROW! Talk about striking while the iron, (or rather, irony) is hot! Won't be anything hot about *that* date, I can tell you. Now, I think he knew about it all along when we went out, got me to agree then ooh, quelle surprise, there happens to be one tomorrow. And guess what, it's for forty-five to fifty-five year olds! Yet another coincidence, I don't think. I know I'm a very grown-up woman and can say, 'No Simon, I have changed my mind,' but then I wouldn't get the feet-tickling or be able to say, 'Yes I tried it once and it was hideous,' because it would be a lie. And he would never, ever shut up about it. Ever. Had to have three

Spanish measures of vodka and tonic so can't write any more.

Saturday 19 January

SPEED DATING — LEST I FORGET!
Every horror story you have ever read, heard or assumed about speed dating is not only TRUE, but multiplied by about a hundred. If you want to maintain any shred of dignity or self-esteem that you mistakenly think you possess, then you MUST NOT go speed dating. Note: never trust Simon's judgement again, about anything at all. I don't even need to write it down as I am sure it will be permanently imprinted on my brain like a fossil, to an extent where, even after my death, scientists removing my brain will be able to interpret every gory detail of the miserable event.

Burping Bulldog: burped at least five times in the space of the four-minute session and said, 'It's me tea,' instead of, 'Excuse my revoltingness.'

Ratman: 'Weekends are no good 'cos I show me rats,' (not a euphemism and what exactly are you showing them?) Continues, 'What with me being secretary of the Gateshead Rat Club.' I rather like rats, but there are limits.

Anorak man: completely devoid of any conversational skills whatsoever. Began with, 'That's a nice necklace,' then launched into a monologue telling me *all* about his job as an engineer and the project he had recently completed from beginning to end, leaving no detail involving pipes, cables or fibre-optics to the imagination. That lasted the full four minutes then heard him trying the necklace compliment on the next woman. Obviously been told to give us some soft-soaping first (not literally of course as that thought is making me retch) before getting down to the nitty-gritty.

Can't be faffed to mention all of them, although every single four-minute slot was equally excruciating. Running through the streets naked would have been preferable and infinitely less embarrassing. But the very worst of them all was...

Younger man: spotted him earlier and thought, 'Ooh things are looking up three down the line', clearly at the fortysomething end of the age range. I know that *for my age* and in twenty watt bulb lighting, I don't look too foul, but alas, I saw 'the look' and was squashed firmly back in my place with the other less attractive fifty-five enders. The look with eyes: dead (post office man) smile: none (he was no actor) face: not one of total indifference, simply one with a message written on it that said, 'Hurry up, not interested, hurry up, not interested,' ad nauseam (probably retching as well). He was obviously there for your 'forty-fiver who looks thirty-five'.

How could I have been so delusional? Feeling extremely invisible. Don't believe your friends when they say, 'But you're gorgeous.' Might look at facial fillers tomorrow. Or laser treatment for lines.

Sunday 20 January

Simon rang at the crack-of. I refused flatly to divulge any details of last night, apart from 'Crap,' and 'You owe me at least twelve hours of feet-tickling.' Can't face reliving that one yet. Looked up facial fillers: 'Treatment can cause redness for two months plus costs a ridiculous amount of money,' basically. Face is bad enough without huge red lines all over it like a living breathing ordnance survey map of the Lake District. No thanks! Sue (ex-colleague Sue) rang to remind me about the Spa Day next Sunday I'd forgotten about for her friend's fiftieth. Dreading it. Will have to dig out old swimsuit and hope against hope that the elastic has, unlike my skin, not perished with age.

Monday 21 January

Absolutely nothing at all happened today.

Tuesday 22 January

Had such a laugh telling Sara all about the speed dating. At least it has entertainment value (at my expense) so not a wholly wasted evening after all. The same applies to holidays too: if it was all lovely, lovely, lovely then no one is remotely interested and the conversation moves on hastily before you can bore them rigid about the unrivalled selection of pastries at breakfast and the incomparable cleanliness of the room. But, if the holiday produced some sort of Basil Fawlty character, or was a candidate for an episode of *Holidays from Hell*, then they are all ears, and rightly so. Might make it a mission to go on disastrous holidays or even start it up as a new business venture in my retirement 'Disaster Holidays — more fun than they sound'? Maybe not. Conjures up images of tsunamis and earthquakes. Will try and think of another title, or business.

Weds 23 January

Centre — the new young man from the other week was there again. Very sweet and friendly. He's a teacher from Colombia and speaks good English. No other details yet. Might try to resurrect some of my 'conversational' Spanish, placed firmly in inverted commas, from the class Twat and I used to go to with the intention of spending long and lazy stretches of time travelling round there in our retirement. More grrrrs!!

Thursday 24 January

Thought a lot about holidays today. Not in a good way. Need a proper retirement treat holiday, like the succession of my couply friends who ritually retire in July then rub every single downtrodden teacher's nose in it by embarking on a world cruise in flaming September when it's:

a) cheap
b) comfortably warm
c) a child-free zone

In addition to *not* going to Spain on a regular basis, I can I see myself *not* going solo on the posh backpacking tour Twat and I had planned. Why not? I feel less confident than I did when I went around Thailand, India and South America alone before starting my first teaching job. On the plus side, surely I'd be:

a) less of a rape target
b) more streetwise
c) able to afford to stay in more salubrious areas

So what's wrong? Maybe it's fear of meeting all those confident, optimistic twentyandthirtysomethings — myself in a former life. Will they make me too envious or conscious of my age? The light's far too bright in those places anyway, it shows up *every* line. Could go on a normal holiday and have everyone look sympathetically over at the token single older (no threat to the under sixties) woman, not daring to strike up a conversation, terrified of getting stuck with her for the whole two weeks.

Maybe a harmless package holiday on an exotic, singles resort — for exotic singles like me — in a dark place like the Arctic Circle in winter is the answer? Oh no, it'd be like two weeks of speed dating dragged out in very slow motion:

slow motion dating. How hideous it would be with everyone working their way through (mentally and platonically of course) the goods on offer. God no! A two-week nightmare — disaster holidays? Yes they already exist, under an assumed name. Angry again — might be hormonal. That's all I need on top of everything else — the flaming menopause!

Friday 25 January

Spent three quarters of today scouring town for a swimsuit that didn't make me look like very white, blotchy sausage meat squeezed clumsily (most likely by hand) into a skin resulting in an uneven texture and in no way fit for even the most modest of sausage making competitions. They exist. I have read about them in Sunday magazines and Fred Elliott, the butcher from *Coronation Street*, once entered one — though it wasn't about the quality it was about the length — ooer! Have gone all double entendre and made myself laugh. Every cloud, as they say. Having had what I would call *partial* success, I brought the semi-offending item back home and spent the remaining quarter of the day preparing my body for public consumption, aka epilating and shaving — enough info.

Don't want to be reminded about this at a future date myself, let alone inflict it upon anyone else who may come across my diary, accidentally or otherwise. Mind you, it would serve them right if they were snooping and, instead of discovering juicy gossip, were subjected to a detailed description of depilation! Yuk.

Saturday 26 January

Sam's been harping on at me (for the lost count-th time) to enrol on courses — *plural*. One damn step at a time please! I really CBA = can't be arsed. Seems to think I'll meet the man of my dreams, who or whatever he is, over Woodcarving for Beginners or Upholstery. She insists that break-time chitchat e.g. 'Can you show me how to deep-button?' or, 'How do you manage to wield such a humongous hammer?' could be the start of a permanent, meaningful relationship. She also naively thinks it might feasibly be the teacher who will make me the object of their evening class desires. Bless her, Sam simply doesn't know the rules: teacher-pupil relationships are ALWAYS an equation: $T=2x$ age of pupil, making any prospective teaching suitor one hundred and ten... I don't think so somehow. Not even *I* am that desperate, or deluded — yet. The awful truth is, I need to fill my days with something so may well have a stab at Art History — if I can ever BA. Opened wine.

That bathroom light is far too bright. I can't possibly, truly, honestly look like that? Salon offering half price Botox. Too scared. Where do they think the 'tox' comes from? Yes — *toxic*. Botox? *NO*TOX ! That's my new slogan. Feel less 'grrr'y tonight due to alcohol. Not the best course of action I know but needs must. I've got that bloody Spa Day tomorrow. You never know, I might come back feeling like a new woman. Trying to be positive this year — finding it a bit of a struggle.

Sunday 27 January

Anyone reading this be warned: Spa Day is *not* for the fainthearted. Now I know what it must feel like to be released from a secure psychiatric unit back into the comfort of your own home. I'm very much appreciating my little house and being alone in it, so I suppose that's one positive to drag out of the day. Started badly from the moment we arrived, having to force down a variety of very strange fruit and vegetable juices for politeness. I mean, 'beetroot juice' — I ask you? Beetroot juice was vinegar in our house. Despite the trauma, I shall attempt to let it go and move on with my life.

After being herded through to the changing area, the inevitable, 'Am I the oldest, saggiest, flabbiest, most sausagey?' panic ensued before covering up with a scary, white hooded bathrobe. Photographic evidence shows we were as frightening as some breakaway wing of the Ku Klux Klan. Suddenly we were all dressed the same and it was at that very moment when the horror dawned: this is what it must feel like to be incarcerated in an institution. Take your pick: a religious cult or eighteenth century nunnery — did they have towelling then? Having plucked up the courage — plucked being the operative word and yes I did promise no details — we de-robed and spent a few minutes in the communal enema, otherwise known as a Jacuzzi. It's vile when you think of all those recently-toileted people sitting bang on top of high speed jets gushing their way into every orifice then out again to circulate in a friendly, sociable manner around the rest of the unfortunate, unsuspecting Jacuzzi-dwellers.

Having survived that 'experience' you are forced to sit around in an unfeasibly hot room reeking of the burning wooden bench that's too boiling to sit on, until your throat dries up and you think you are going to spontaneously combust (yes I know it wouldn't be spontaneous if you knew it was about to occur but I don't make the rules). Before the combustion happens, which I am convinced that it must do with a reasonable amount of regularity but doesn't make the news because of a conspiracy between the spa owners and local press, you are dragged out and instructed to cover yourself in ICE! I mean, talk about inducing a heart attack! At that point I decided I would rather be changing children's pooed-in pants back at school than be there. And I paid dearly for the privilege. At least they paid *me* at school.

Lunch: shepherded up to the restaurant like a train of sheep to the slaughter (too old to be lambs) where there were large groups of similarly robed inmates and – shock horror — MEMBERS OF THE GENERAL PUBLIC in normal attire! We were clearly on some sort of phasing-in programme, preparing us for release later on in the day. More weird food was served: tofu and superfood salad (a contradiction in terms, anyone knows there is nothing super about any salad) containing exotic peas that had clearly never seen the inside of a freezer. All yuk. After a stint in a very steamy (sadly literally and not in any way sexy) sweaty torture chamber stinking of nasal spray, we were frogmarched to our 'treatment'. On balance, I think I would prefer the electric shock variety over what happened next. Yet more torture ensued as I was massaged within an inch of my life, but what was in store for us after that, I am struggling to come to terms with and keep asking myself, 'Did that actually happen or am I having false memory syndrome?' I am afraid to report that it did.

I was escorted to a 'sleep room', and ordered to lie in a bed complete with sheets and fluffy blankets for the next fifteen minutes with 'sound waves' as they were referred to, vibrating through the mattress. Now let's make one thing crystal clear — I'm no Einstein but I know categorically that sound waves are inaudible. Call me a pedant if you must. I collapsed in a fit of giggles and had to bury my head in the fluffy, fleecy blanket so as not to disturb the other sleeping patients. UNBELIEVABLE! I lasted about five minutes in there before I had to escape, like a naughty child or a fee-paying criminal. Do *not* get me started again on the cost!

Not sure which is worse, speed dating or Spa Daying. A draw I think. At least speed dating is shorter. Great to be back in the real world. Feeling shattered after all the so-called pampering and relaxation — not the desired effect. I must put a marker in this page in case anyone suggests a

Spa Day and the true memory of it, like the pain of childbirth, has faded from my mind.

Tuesday 29 January

It's Tuesday and I am still recovering from Spa Day. How did I know nothing of its true horrors before? I feel betrayed, as though a friend has taken you to be waterboarded when you were expecting to go surfboarding. Then it dawned on me, I missed the sign that said 'Welcome to Spa Day. The first rule of Spa Day is: you don't talk about Spa Day.' Must have been on the wall, obscured by the shelves, brimming with 'Cold Pressed Organic Culinary Avocado Oil'.

Weds/Wednesday 30 January

Realised how lazy I am as I never write 'Wednesday' — apart from then — because generally I CBA. Although it contains only one more letter than both Thursday and Saturday, I suppose a line has to be drawn somewhere. However, as part of my efforts to be less idle, from this day forth I shall write 'Wednesday'. Having said all that, I didn't do anything noteworthy today or yesterday. Spa Day well and truly wiped me out, not the intended outcome I'm sure.

February

Friday 1 February

Had a great morning at the Centre! Was really looking forward to it after a lull in the week. Well when I say 'lull' I mean utter mind-blowing boredom. In fact it never managed to get off the ground after Sunday. Clearly it was God's punishment for my having too much fun at the spa. Nevertheless, I settled a score with that God fella because Lucas, the Colombian guy, was there. He was so friendly and open. After telling him I was a teacher he recounted the dreadful tale that led him to seek asylum here.

Lucas's Story

He'd been a primary school teacher and the union rep for his school. There was a big campaign for a pay rise, led by his union, but as this was an election year it didn't go down well with the government — to put it mildly. Lucas was well aware of this, but told me how little money teachers earned there and how it was becoming increasingly difficult to feed a family on the salary. Luckily, he had no family to support, which makes it even more admirable that he was prepared to risk going to prison in order to help others. An unrivalled level of selflessness. I always felt smug and self-righteous when I took part in strike action to improve conditions but all I was losing was a day's pay... not my liberty, or worse. Ignoring anonymous death threats, Lucas led the strike.

    The next day he was arrested without charge and spent three long weeks in prison. He was beaten on several occasions but left alone during the last week. As a result he had no visual proof of the injuries inflicted upon him. The bruises had faded. The scars, however, were hidden deep inside his psyche. Upon release, he was threatened again.

Lucas knew what could happen to trade union activists who ignored warnings. He had seen it before.

When he returned to school he learned that two of his colleagues, also close friends, had been sacked. Two men, one single, one married with two children; no one had heard from them since. It was no coincidence that, despite the risks, they had been campaigning for Lucas's release, such was their loyalty. Lucas knew that they too would have been illegally imprisoned so began asking questions of those in authority as to their whereabouts. A week later he returned home from school to find a hand-delivered envelope containing a bullet and a note. The message translated as, 'In answer to your questions. See you soon.'

From then on he knew he must leave. He couldn't put any more of his colleagues' lives in danger, nor could he sit back and say nothing as that would be mental torture to a man of such strong principles. He would not be the first political activist to make himself invisible in order to survive. So he went into hiding, waited for news of his two colleagues who were released from prison after another week, then fled the country. Listening to his heart-wrenching tale of leaving his family and friends, a job he loved, and his students who adored him — a man of passion, of commitment both to his values and to helping others — it makes me ashamed of my own self-pity. Pathetic, churlish, like a spoilt child moaning to a friend about the quality of their Christmas presents when the friend has recently lost both parents in a car crash. Thank God I was born in a country that allows freedom of speech. You can shout at any government to your heart's content, not that they'll listen, but at least you won't get imprisoned, beaten up and threatened with your life.

And now he is under further scrutiny — having to prove that he truly is a marked man, facing death should he return to his own country. I can't imagine anything more terrifying! Yet here is this outwardly calm, polite, gentle man, portraying his story in such a way that it sounded like it was about someone else; matter of fact. Humbling — and in an accent I could listen to all day.

When I left, Lucas thanked me for helping him! I was embarrassed because the legal team are the people who are *truly* helping this man, but I suppose being supportive, offering a sympathetic ear, must be comforting to people there. It was very thoughtful of him. Some people, apparently, haven't written me off quite yet.

Saturday 2 February

RIGHT — THAT'S IT! NEVER going back to the Whiskey Jar ever again! This takes the bloody biscuit — could do with one right now, or a whiskey for that matter. I have been going since I was a student, since it first opened, and it's always been one of my favourite haunts. Birthday parties, bands, countless get-togethers and unforgettable evenings spent with a myriad of friends. It pains me to say it but if Lucas can leave everything for his principles, then so can I. Hmm, sounding like the spoilt brat analogy again. Apologies Lucas — and to all other political prisoners, I know it's trivial by comparison. *But*, as if being ignored by the male population isn't bad enough, it seems that I am also invisible to women! Or rather, I am visible but regularly need to be reminded of my current status in society, lest I get ideas above my station.

There I was, the only person at the bar, being served by the young woman and about to order some food for Sam and me – assuming that, 'Yes please?' means, 'What do you want, I'm all ears?' when, from the other end of the counter there comes a male voice shouting, 'Two pints of lager please!' at which point she, without a word, puts down the pen she has poised to take *my* order and goes to serve him instead! 'Gobsmacked' doesn't go anywhere near it, though someone of a more violent disposition (or with PMT, perhaps) may well have slapped the woman in the face. What did I do? I said nothing and merely beckoned to Sam, who took over whilst I sat down then made her listen to exactly how I felt in great detail for the next twenty minutes. Then, as the flames of wrath were beginning to die down, she decided to pour proverbial petrol on them — that stuff's not cheap either — by asking 'Mum, do you think your hormones are affecting you?' After practically savaging her to death (verbally of course) I calmed myself and managed to convince her that the problem lay entirely at the feet of society: people not progesterone! That would make a good slogan – not sure what for though. Secretly, I think it could be a dangerous cocktail of both, but not admitting to that one. It's staying where it belongs, under the carpet.

Speaking of cocktails — I'm getting up to have a medicinal vodka and tonic. Does that constitute a cocktail? It definitely would do to the manager of the best pub in Morpeth who, when asked for a white wine and soda, replied that he didn't 'sorve curktails' — in his inimitable style and Northumbrian accent!

Now I feel like an angry shouting-at-the-telly woman , only without the 'at-the-telly' bit. Instead I am shouting into my diary. Is that better or worse? Suppose it's more environmentally friendly for the neighbours in terms of noise pollution, but I am using up trees. Probably a draw.

Sunday 3 February

Day started well: Sam called in bearing cakes! She's worried I may be cracking up — maybe I am? No, I'm merely finding it hard to adjust to life — to retired life, to a life alone, to my age, and she knows I'm going to rail against any injustice along the way. I try to convince her that it's fine, *I'm* fine and the moment she thinks it's safe, she begins the 'ground offensive', a military style campaign to which she is totally committed and determined to see through to the bitter end until the target, i.e. me, has surrendered. Carefully and strategically positioned, with her back covered (nearly out of the front door) she casually throws the grenade at my feet by saying, 'If I come round on Tuesday and show you how to upload music to your phone will you sign up to '2gether.com' ?' What on earth's the matter with calling it 'Together.com'? It's pure laziness. And because I simply couldn't BA to argue, stunned and shell-shocked from the assault, I simply nodded, robotically. God, what have I let myself in for?

How did Tony Benn write all those diaries, year after year after year? I was pleased to note that he didn't write it every day and sometimes wrote about the whole week at once which, to the pedant, would be considered as cheating because 'diario' in Spanish means 'daily', not weekly. Shit, I *am* that pedant! I ought to get out more. I suppose Tony had an interesting life. *Any* life would be a bonus to me. After all, 'Lunch with Simon' doesn't quite have the same ring to it as 'Lunch with Nelson Mandela'. However interesting Simon may be, the occasion isn't noteworthy by comparison. Still, everything is relative and this is my life now so I have to accept it. I shall do my best to make it interesting. That is my promise to myself. Whether I succeed in keeping it remains to be seen. We have one life and mustn't waste it wallowing in self-pity. I will try, though it feels like a mammoth task at this moment. Not sure that 2gether.com is the answer...

Monday 4 February

Oh God! Mondays are bad enough without meeting up with Hilary. Here I go, more self-pity — not a good start to the new regime! I had to do it. Could no longer say, 'No, I've got too much marking to do,' or, 'I'm up early tomorrow, will have to pass,' or 'I'm out at a staff meeting until late.'

Nor could I say (as some brave Americans who've been on assertiveness training courses would do) 'No, Hilary. I'm feeling low enough these days and don't relish the prospect of being dragged down to the brink of suicide by your own negativity, thank you!' or words to that effect. Hilary is an old and dear friend, but a drain, as Mum would have said. 'There are two types of people in this life: radiators and drains.' As I am quite partial to a plumbing reference, I have adopted this and cruelly put people into one box or the other. Of course, everyone wants to think of themselves as a radiator, myself included. A radiator emits warmth, makes you feel good about yourself, is an energy-giving person who you want to spend time with. A drain does the opposite. A drain will sap your energy and quash your enthusiasm with their self-obsession. A drain is not in the least bit interested in what you have to say, even if it's about them. Often the friendship survives out of pure habit, and we know about Bruce and his old habits. I fear I may be becoming a drain. The stark realisation has hit me after mentioning the drain theory. I am sure my friends would disagree to my face, but I wouldn't dare to ask them.

Unlike the saying 'two brains are better than one,' two drains are most certainly *not*. Two negatives, in this case, most definitely do not make a positive when it comes to post-retired, hopefully *pre*-menopausal women. We all have them: old friends who you love to bits because you have shared experiences and history. However, people change, life changes. Some move on and some, like Hilary, do not. I have always been a forward-looking, positive person and now I feel like I have turned into a Hilary, aka Moaning Minnie. Yes I know, diary readers, whoever you may be, I have done little else *but* moan since I started unburdening, but this isn't the real me. Or, horror of horrors, could it be that this is not merely the result of a life change or (possible) hormonal change, but a wholesale personality change? Extremely worried now. Might even describe it as 'hashtag extremely worried,' as Sam would say.

I digress — back to today. We met up, and for the very first time in thirty years of knowing Hilary, she asked me a series of questions! Maybe it's her new year's resolution, to feign interest in other people and lull them into a false sense of security. This would have been all well and good had I been leading a full and active life and was reasonably happy, but when I'm not...well that's another matter entirely. Sadly, I had little to say or offer and it was almost a relief when the question list was used up and the silence was cued for me to ask about work. I used to avoid that like the plague; enquiring about Hilary's work, was simply sealing your own fate because she has the most boring job: 'project manager' in an electronics factory, not even doing up houses or art projects, all business stuff accompanied by annoying, incomprehensible business speak. And if you ask, she will tell. Every last, excruciating detail. On this occasion, though, I didn't mind as it made my life of doing practically zilch seem considerably more preferable to doing a lot of very boring things. It also filled in the time. When the topic moved on to what her neighbours' kids (whom I've never met) were doing now in their careers, I made my excuses ('Sam is coming round,' a lie) to the resounding tut-tutting in my head from the American assertiveness trainers, aka the smug idiots. What do they know about the British cultural compunction to weave a complicated web of lies that will later trap you and send you into a spin, all in order to spare someone's feelings?

Dreading tomorrow. Sam will descend, hell bent on 2bloodygether.com. Not in the right frame of mind for that. More lowering of self-esteem will ensue. Same theory applies: get your head down and get on with it to appease them. They can't badger me once I've tried it and scientifically proven that it's a disaster.

Tuesday 5 February

What a farce! Sam showed me how to up or download music, whichever it is, to my phone. With one arm twisted up my back, I reluctantly signed up for masochism — not the *Fifty Shades of Grey* kind, at least I hope not! It's so dreadful, you have to see if anyone has 'winked' at you — yes w.i.n.k.e.d — which I find utterly ridiculous for a start. Alternatively, you are at liberty to wink at someone else, so I can't criticise it for being sexist, merely stupid. Sam checked it about ten minutes before she left, bless her. As if a three-deep virtual queue of eligible men would have formed, singing 'I've been waiting for a girl like you,' a la Foreigner (circa 1980s). Alas, it was winkerless. Breathed a huge secret sigh of relief.

Wednesday 6 February

In a boredom-induced moment of madness today I looked up *twat* in an online dictionary. Yes I know it's sad but it brightened up my day no end. Hear me out before you judge:
A man who is a stupid, incompetent fool. Synonyms: bozo, cuckoo, fathead, goof, goofball, goose, jackass, zany.
The Americanisms make it funnier and infinitely more pertinent to *the* Twat. Scoffed millions of salt and vinegar crisps plus a sensible English (cutting down) measure of vodka and tonic by way of celebration.

Friday 8 February

Desperately sad day. Minika was in tears when I went into the Centre. Sobbing quietly to herself, whilst the few men who were there looked down at their feet awkwardly. A mix of cultures, unsure of the most appropriate course of action to take with someone they barely knew. Understandably, they did nothing. The atmosphere was strange; everyone was silent. Then the bombshell was dropped. The devastating news was delivered by Lucas who, in spite of his caring manner, could do nothing to soften the blow or ease the pain of it.

Jakub is dead — shot, perhaps by another young boy, but there are no details. His cousin managed to relay the news via Jakub's campaigners to publicise it as evidence of how dangerous the Democratic Republic of Congo is. Once a boy, now a death; one of many. A boy, invisible here as a human but entirely visible as a statistic; a propaganda tool to bandy about. Hooray! One less for their records. Hooray! We are getting rid of them, sending them back, who cares what will become of them? They are not our problem. Lucas was shaken. He didn't know Jakub but his words were, 'But for the grace of God.' He is a man of faith. I felt the need to tell him Jakub's story, as a tribute to his immense bravery during his short life.

Jakub's Story

Taken from his parents at the age of fifteen, Jakub was a child soldier. He was forcibly recruited and underwent horrendous abuse in an attempt to desensitise him. If you want children to murder one another, they mustn't feel anything at all. But they never broke this boy. They failed to carry out their heinous plans to turn him into a killing machine. A particularly intelligent boy, Jakub was one of the few people of his age able to speak English, his third language — Lingala being his first and French his second. He had taught himself from a treasured book and CD given by an aid worker. How proud he was of his achievement, too! During his time with us at the Centre he rarely spoke of the horrors he'd endured or the violence he had witnessed, and undoubtedly been a victim of himself. An extraordinary stroke of luck befitting of such a special boy, enabled him to escape his captors before he was forced to kill others, before his training was complete.

One evening he was in Kinshasa, the nearest city and capital of DRC, with his kidnappers, the soldiers. They were picking up supplies for the camp when Jakub spotted a British children's charity truck, parked beside a café. He told his captors he was going to use the café toilet and managed to climb out of the window, found the charity truck and secreted himself away under the tarpaulin. Miraculously, the truck was not stopped or searched and the two aid workers arrived at their lodgings some distance from the city. Though they spoke French, Jakub impressed them, not merely with his English, but with his remarkable courage and determination. He begged them to help him escape, not to France, to Britain.

Everyone knew that if this boy were to return to his home town the militia would find and kill him for attempting escape. This brave young man, officially a child at sixteen years of age, wanted to make another life for himself in a country thousands of miles from his home. Others he knew of had managed to escape to neighbouring countries and were in hiding there, hoping that when the situation improved they could return home. But Jakub wasn't prepared to waste his life in hope. He wanted to work, to study, to improve himself. The charity workers told him they couldn't help individuals in this way but his persistence and likeability wore them down and, at great personal risk, they agreed to help him.

Passport and papers secured, he was put on a plane to London then dispersed to Newcastle. Ecstatic at his escape, if somewhat culture-shocked, one of his favourite sayings on arriving in the depths of a North Eastern winter was, 'It's friggin' freezin', man!' always accompanied by a cheery grin. One of the paid workers at the Centre, Ken, advised him that 'flippin' might be better than 'friggin', contrary to what he heard — and worse — many times on the street!

Jakub was a fast learner, a keen worker, brimming with youthful energy. A joker, a 'live wire' as Ken fondly called him.

He waited such a long time for his asylum application to be processed that he had turned seventeen. His status as a child offered him protection: a room in a hostel, where he was. He found a job, prepping food in a kitchen of a small restaurant, telling them that he would be head chef there one day. The chef liked him. Everyone liked him. He was grateful to be alive, working, not killing. Learning skills, not maiming and torturing his fellow citizens, his friends, other children. Then Jakub's world came crashing down on him — once he turned eighteen there was no longer any obligation to help. An adult overnight. On paper, able to stand on his own two feet with no support or refuge. Despite the situation in his own country and what they would do to him for escaping, for deserting their armed group if he returned, a deportation order was issued and he was forcibly removed from the country, via a prison-like detention centre.

That happened shortly after I began volunteering at the Centre. I only met him on a few occasions, but enough to feel as if I knew him as well as the others did. The government were bowing to pressure from the media, the electorate who complained about immigration, blaming refugees and migrant workers on a lack of resources — the obvious scapegoats. The government needed to be seen flexing its muscles, massaging the statistics to regain popularity. Jakub was a casualty of this; a political, unjust war.

We campaigned against his removal. We petitioned and wrote letters to MPs, to anyone who could help, but were ignored by those at the top. We wrote to him in the detention centre. I shed floods of tears over that boy — tears of anger, of sadness, of guilt and finally, of hopelessness. Jakub was deported on the twenty-seventh of December.

Saturday 9 February

Shi-i-it! I sound like my friend whose granddaughter's first words were 'Oh gog' meaning 'Oh God' because, as I would have done, my friend blasphemed constantly from the stress of looking after a young child again. The supermarket queue was extra-long one day and the baby exclaimed loudly, 'Oh go-o-og!' This, however, is altogether more serious. This is a definite shi-i-it: two men have 'winked' at me! I examined their profiles and they both look vaguely human and have similar interests to mine. What now? At least I have something to talk about when I next see Sara or Simon and they'll be impressed that I've been proactive when, if truth be told, I have been press-ganged into it by my own flesh and blood. Maybe that will be enough to placate them for now…who am I kidding?

Dave — why is everyone called Dave or, almost as common, Pete? Dave, I shall call him Dave One in case there are others. Is that being optimistic — a veritable queue of Daves or pessimistic — bound to be a non-starter so will need to trawl around for a Dave Two? I can't decide. Moving on, Dave One is a Systems Analyst — cue the groan. I have never known, nor do I wish to know, what that means. Do you go from place to place analysing people's systems? What type of systems, exactly? Education? Interesting. Computer? Boring. Filing? Unlikely. Accountancy? Desperate. More likely to be none of the above. One thing's for sure — I *won't* be asking for details. The interests, on the other hand, are compatible on paper of course: travelling — tick. Fair-weather walking — tick. Cinema — cross. Theatre — tick-ish. Eating — mega-tick.

Have ignored all sensible online dating advice i.e. 'email exchanges may help to get to know one another before deciding to meet' and have cut to the chase. Why waste time? I can email my friends any day. I don't email friends from the past enough. The last thing I need is anyone else to bloody email. Hopefully he won't turn up and I can tell people I tried my best now leave me in peace. Mind you, I need something of vague interest to happen if I'm ever going to fill up the pages of this diary. And I'm now curious. So, suggested coffee on Wednesday. Don't want to appear too keen. Then bed. NO I DID NOT SUGGEST BED! What I mean is I came to bed before he replied, thus sending cool and casual vibes.

Sunday 10 February

Sh-i-it! Response from Dave One: affirmative! Now ultra-nervous. Totally regretting it now. Blaming it on the glass of wine. It made me do it. Not guilty, Your Honour. Need to calm down and be rational: it's for a coffee and he will (I hope) feel as terrified as I do — or will he? What if he's arrogant and cocky, or one of those alpha male arseholes who I can't stand? There's no section on the form that says, 'Are you an arrogant twat?' Tick .You have to take your chance on that one. THINK POSITIVE LIZZIE, THINK POSITIVE! I used to be the optimistic, outward-looking type. Now I'm struggling.

Monday 11 February

Spent today telling people about the date. Mistake number one. But my motivation was boredom and a desperate attempt to sound interesting. Also, I was trying to make some sort of effort — yes, and to shut them all up! Had to have wine to help me keep calm. And induce sleep. Not too much though, don't want to rock up looking extra-foul with a hangover: coffee? Yes, make mine large and black with two paracetamol.

Tuesday 12 February

Go-o-og! AWFUL! Awful, awful, awful:

a) had lied about age — fifty-eight for him had come at least a decade ago
b) barely recognisable from photo i.e. photo — a shock of dark hair, real life Dave One: absolutely no hair plus grey beard
c) talked all about the work he used to do (retired, unsurprisingly at his age) despite the fact that I deliberately did not ask him about it

He also performed Hilary's trick of, 'Well enough about me, let's talk about me,' by asking me a question and using it as a bridge in order to continue the monologue: 'I see you're a retired teacher, what did you teach?' After my one word response of, 'Primary,' that was the end of the questioning and the floodgates re-opened with, 'Oh, I thought about primary school teaching once but...' blah, blah, bloody blah. INCESSANT. Had to resort to bare-faced lying in the end. Don't start, all you assertiveness–trained Americans! I told him Twat had died in order to avoid mentioning the other 'd' word and hearing all about his own divorce. It had the desired effect of silencing him for a split second of respite. When he insisted on paying for the coffees I temporarily suspended my feminist instincts and didn't object because I damn well earned every drop.

DISASTER. Never thought I'd say this but at least speed dating is only four minutes of torture, although it's *twelve* times four minutes at least. About evens on the horror stakes, then. Be positive: he wasn't a serial killer (though he could have been — they always seem normal, apparently). He wasn't nasty and was keen to see me again. Of course he wanted to see me again: a silent stooge fifteen plus years his junior. Dave One's ideal woman.

Thursday 14 February

Valentine's Day — oh the awful irony of it after the events of this week! 'Lucky Lizzie's Quest for Romance', a two-page-turner.

Friday 15 February

A weird day at the Centre. Left me unsure of what to think; such a mixture of good and bad. Michael was there when I arrived; strong caring Michael, comforting Minika. Lucas took me to one side and explained that someone spat at Minika as she was about to get off the top deck of the bus. A violent act committed by a young man on his own. Racism at its absolute worst. But what happened next was unexpected: instead of turning their heads, ignoring it, feigning blindness as often happens in difficult situations, the passengers, led by an 'older lady', rounded on the assailant. 'Older lady' stood in front of him blocking his way to the stairs, fearless, and demanded, 'Why did you do that? It's disgusting!' As he began to emit a torrent of abuse, two younger men grabbed him from behind, brought him swiftly to the floor and restrained him, shouting, 'Racist pig!' as he struggled like a fish on the dirty, wet floor of the bus.

Meanwhile, the other passengers leapt into action: one alerted the driver to what was happening; another called the police while others consoled Minika. How I wish I had been on that bus, but maybe it's fortunate that I wasn't, considering my current emotional state, or I may well have been writing this from a police cell: 'Evidently this one went radgey. GBH is the charge, Sarge.' Do you think they ever say that in real police stations to brighten up their shift because it rhymes and sounds silly, or is it restricted to badly researched TV crime drama?

The police had arrived quickly, relieving the two heavy heroes of their public-spirited duties and carted the guy away, to resounding applause from the remaining passengers who were now 'all in this together'! I would love to have seen that: united against racism, standing up to a bully, community spirit in action. Minika had to give a statement but was adamant that she didn't want to press charges or 'make a fuss' as she put it, terrified of jeopardising her chances of gaining refugee status. 'I don't want to cost the country more money,' she said to Lucas. When he told her that it was the law-breaking attacker who would be doing that, she simply shrugged, saying that she was happy and grateful to the passengers, that she'd never expected it and felt his humiliation was enough for her. A most humbling attitude indeed. Compared to all she has suffered recently at the hands of despicable, depraved individuals from her own country who would never be brought to justice, being spat upon pales into insignificance.

Minika's Story

Her name means 'calmness' in Efik, the language of the region where her parents were born. In search of work and a better education for their child, the family moved to Lagos when Minika was a baby. Tragically, both parents were killed in a bus crash when she was seventeen. Minika was named well. How can someone who has endured such trauma in their young life, and whose future is full of uncertainty, remain so calm?

Old enough to support herself, Minika was forced to leave college when her parents died. Like most other poor Nigerians, there was no life insurance or compensation package for her. Soon afterwards, she found a job as a hotel receptionist and managed to survive alone in the family home. A few years later, something happened that, at the time, she innocently assumed would be her very worst nightmare: the hotel closed down due to the world recession. Unable to pay the rent, Minika decided to ask an aunt and uncle if she could stay with them. However, when she went to visit, her aunt was very upset and confided in her that her husband was gambling and had racked up enormous debts as a consequence. How could she possibly ask for help in those circumstances?

Soon afterwards she was approached in the centre of Lagos by a smart, officious woman claiming to be from a recruitment agency who offered her a receptionist's job in a hotel in London. The cover story was that she remembered Minika from the hotel she used to work in and had been impressed by her skills and professionalism. Then, by 'coincidence', noticed her walking down the street that day. Tricked. Duped. Lured by the promise of a wonderful new start, at a point in her life when she desperately needed it, Minika jumped at the chance. The bogus agency provided false documents and a passport with a new name. She has never disclosed that name to anyone as she wants to forget everything about the events that followed. Eager to please those who held the key to a new and exciting future, she believed the gang when they told her that the new identity would make it easier to obtain a work visa. In fact, it was done so that she would disappear without any risk to her traffickers of Minika being traced by her aunt, or by anyone else for that matter. There was no recruitment agency, no hotel, no job. Instead, Minika became enslaved in the sex industry.

Later, she learned that it was her uncle who had sold her to the gang. Betrayed by a member of her own family to service a gambling debt. He had told them about her circumstances, how desperate she was and where to find her. Looking back, she told me that she'd found two things strange: one was that they never told her the name of the hotel she was supposedly destined for, only that it was in central London; the other was that she wondered why such a hotel would employ a Nigerian woman with less than perfect English as a receptionist, when there was a shortage of jobs in Britain. She had read about the recession affecting the whole of Europe too. But why would you question what appeared to be a dream come true? Salvation, not only from unemployment, but from the difficult political and economic situation in her own country. An opportunity for a new life in Europe. An adventure. The dream, of course, rapidly transformed into a nightmare.

They met her at Heathrow Airport. Immigration were satisfied with the false documentation and she was taken, not to a hotel, but to a dank, windowless basement room and locked in. When she screamed to be out they silenced her with drugs and raped her repeatedly. The first rapists were her captors — people from her own country — followed by a constant stream of men of all nationalities. How does anyone cope with that? I cannot begin to imagine the horror of it all. How does this incredibly resilient young woman manage to function and move on with her life after such brutality and unspeakable trauma?

After a few months of torture: sedated and beaten, forced to have sex with scores of vile men, Minika mustered up the little physical and mental strength she had left in her damaged, weakened body and planned her escape. One day she kept the drugs they pushed into her under her tongue and didn't swallow them. It meant she could now talk coherently and begged the last client of the night for chewing gum, pressing it into the keyhole when he left, locking the door after him as instructed by the gang. The next morning they came to take her to shower (for the customers' benefit, not for her own wellbeing) and had to break the lock. Ingenious! Minika pretended to be in a deep sleep so the gang returned to the upper floors to argue over who should mend the lock. At great risk to her safety, she courageously stole out of the room, up the stairs and found the front door unlocked! How terrifying it must have been, running through the streets, barefoot. Running for your life, like a scene from a film, not daring to look behind. She finally flagged down a police car and she was driven to a police station. In short, by the time Minika had identified the house (having seen it once from the outside in the dead of night) the men had fled the place leaving no clues as to their identities. Her captors had already moved on to ply their filthy trade elsewhere.

Minika claimed asylum and, through the dispersal system, found herself here in Newcastle. She is also hoping to be successful in her application for Leave to Remain status, which would mean that she could stay in the country for the next five years. Bravely naming her uncle as party to her trafficking, she knew that her life would be in danger from then on. Sex trafficking is a hugely lucrative, repugnant business. It was possible that the traffickers may have already killed her uncle, if they had not recouped their expenses on their investment: the fee they paid him, the false documents and hefty travel costs. Returning to Lagos was *not* an option. They would be sure to murder or recapture her, given the chance, and they would start by searching her home town.

You read about these things in the news, watch TV documentaries on the subject 'with scenes that some viewers may find disturbing', but you never expect to meet someone who has actually lived through it. Such is life at the Refugee Centre. It opens your eyes to the darker side of the world in which we live. Trauma buried beneath a smile, masked by a laugh. Terror beneath a countenance of calm. And here I am — moping about my life not panning out quite as perfectly as I had planned. At least my life has never been in danger, unlike many of theirs. I am ashamed of my self-indulgence.

Sunday 17 February

Massive blow today. I am bloody fuming! Sam phoned and said that Twat had announced he was buying her a car — a brand new Mini, no less, for her birthday next week! She was trying to tell me calmly as if reporting a fact, like a newsreader, but she couldn't hide her excitement. Trying to buy *her* more like. Bastard. Forced me into a minimal divorce settlement, despite the fact that I was earning far less than he was. Yes, as is often the case, my career break spent raising *our* daughter — at *his* behest, I may add — meant I missed out on promotion. I never wanted the break. I wanted to work, and our mums would have both helped. I could have gone part-time, even in those days, which would have kept me in the loop. But no — he remembered how nice it was to have Mummy there all the time, leaving no whim unpandered to, turning him into the spoilt adult brat that he is today.

As a result of indulging him, I suffered in the long run. My career stagnated and he pleaded poverty in the settlement by, what do they call it, 'creative accountancy', aka lying. I was left with less than I was entitled to, no savings, and a reduced pension from the career break I never wanted in the first place! And now, *now* he wants to buy Sam's affections with money that should have been mine. Bitter? Moi? Calm, calm, calm, calm ...

3.00 a.m. Need to write. It's become my therapy. No I do not need frigging therapy. I need to get a grip. How exactly do you do that? Does anyone out there know? I'm angry and now I can't sleep. Doubly angry. Mum used to have a brandy if she couldn't sleep. I wonder if vodka has the same effect? I shall try it in the name of science, naturally.

Monday 18 February

Woke up feeling as rough as the bottom of a budgie's cage. Very few people keep budgies nowadays, in those tiny cages, poor things. You sometimes see them in aviaries but luckily the little old lady budgie generation has passed on, leaving us only with a simile to remember them by. I overdid the experiment but I can categorically state that vodka has the same sleep-inducing features as brandy. So, we all learned something. I am being side-tracked by the budgies. I also woke up having dark thoughts about Twat. So much so that if I *do* end up murdering him, as I really want to, the police psychologists, expertly guided by any random diary readers, can trace it back to this day when the thoughts first popped into my twisted brain.

Didn't do much today except lie around nursing what was, in reality, a hangover but I like to refer to it as my 'lack of sleep headache'. Same thing, I suppose. Tried not to think about Twat during the day. Distracted myself by watching daytime TV... mistake! Every advert was geared towards people who aren't merely retired, but all require propping up in some way or another by various forms of moving furniture: hospital-style beds; stair-lifts; chairs that go up, down, round, in and out then make tea for you. Programmes such as *I've found something upstairs to sell so I can go on a cruise*. Don't get me started on cruises — if I see another advert featuring smiley, silver-haired people pretending to enjoy themselves on what amounts to a floating prison, I will vomit! I can think of few things worse than being stuck in the middle of the sea with the same bunch, day in day out; each of them secretly wondering who will be so honoured as to sit at the captain's table tonight.

All in all another waste of a day. They are becoming too frequent. Must do more.

Wednesday 20 February

I need to help myself and stop moping. Like a scary psychic, Sam called in and thrust yet another adult education brochure in my hand today. Not in the right frame of mind for that yet but I flicked through it, initially out of politeness then became engrossed in the sheer volume and range of courses, skills, qualifications and *the* most bizarre list of one-off sessions I have ever held in my hand:
Accountancy Level 1 (not at all bizarre)
Accountancy Level 2 (get the picture?)
Further down:
A Sugar Paste Plaque (a *what*? Tempted to go, get a brief glimpse of one from a safe distance to satisfy my curiosity then scarper!)
Edible Easter Figures (a one-off)
Well there wouldn't be much demand for it in June or September, I expect!

Despite my ridiculing, Easter is fast approaching and I am absolutely fascinated by the prospect of a chocolate Pontius Pilate whose Chantilly cream-filled head you could spitefully bite off and spit out immediately after he has ordered that marzipan Jesus be crucified, thus wiping the slate clean and delighting all of your Christian friends you have invited round for the occasion.

Friday 22 February

A relatively calm day at the Centre after the trauma of last week and Minika's horrendous experience on the bus. She has bounced back as if nothing happened. Many of us would be reluctant to go out of the house and be in need of counselling following such a hate crime, but not Minika. It lifted my spirits a little.

Saturday 23 February

In an attempt to distract myself from Sam's birthday bribe which she will arrive in tomorrow, I forced myself to go into town to buy her a present. It's not that I resent buying my lovely daughter anything, it's just that everything is an effort these days. Taking Sam out for lunch and trying to look forward to it. I'm surprised Twat didn't demand to monopolise her for the day in exchange for the lavish, ridiculously over-the-top gift. Mind you, I didn't ask her what she was doing in the evening.

I bought her a necklace she'd admired a few weeks ago and some of her favourite perfume. Spent more than I usually do. I couldn't help myself but didn't want to appear mean compared with Daddy Moneybags. I hate him for that.

Sunday 24 February

A lovely birthday lunch at the pizza place not far from my house, arranged deliberately to avoid the necessity of driving. It was irritating enough having to look at the damn thing parked outside. I tried to be kind and managed to say it was 'lovely' so as not to spoil Sam's birthday excitement like a malevolent wretch but it was bloody hard work! Despite there being only the two of us, I think she enjoyed it and I exhausted myself trying to be upbeat. Sam's single at the moment but I can't imagine it will be for long. It's not that she needs to have a suitor in tow, far from it; she simply attracts one after another! Says she wants to enjoy some 'girlfriend time' — we shall see. She was meeting her friends for a drink later. I was secretly relieved that Twat wasn't having the pleasure of her company for the evening.

Wednesday 27 February

Email from the disaster dating site! Wonder if I should suggest a merger with my thriving 'Disaster Holidays' business? Toyed with the idea of deleting it — can I be bothered with all of this? Don't think I'm ready or in a 'good place' as they say, but I have to make an effort, for the sake of the diary if nothing else. I did it all for you, dear diary — and to placate my nearest and dearest, obviously. I hope they appreciate it. They all, with the exception of you, dearest diary, said, 'If there's no spark with the dating site men you can always just be friends.' Why? I pointed out that I neither need nor want any more friends — I haven't used up the ones I've got yet. Forced myself to open it, out of curiosity, you understand, not desire.
Ian — looks semi-reasonable:

head — one
eyes — two, not three
hair — ignore, hence the *semi*-reasonable
fifty-four — probably a lie

Wants to meet up. None of this emailing foreplay nonsense. More like, 'Let's get on with it and check each other out,' attitude. Quite like that — not that I'm interested. Well I was less interested before I read 'Freelance Journalist'. Now I'm a teeny weeny bit more interested. Maybe he's *too* interesting for me. DO NOT DO YOURSELF DOWN. I used to be interesting — once. Checked diary: two items — one was the dentist (does that count?) It does when you're scratching around for things to pass the time. The other was Sam for lunch. 'Simon theatre?' crossed out due to better offer, for him, not me — a young barman from one of his local haunts.

So, Mr Journo, I am prepared to meet you next week. Mustn't hurry, especially if he's looking all keen. Monday is next week. No, that sounds too desperate. Tuesday then! Don't want to appear overly keen myself or discourage him *too* much, not after the last one. Sharpen that pencil and get ready to take note. Oh God I sound so cool, calm and confident. I am feeling physically sick at the thought. How exactly do you quantify the optimum amount of encouragement?

A new month soon and a new start, perhaps?

Thursday 28 February

Made myself wait until the afternoon to email and arranged to meet on Tuesday! There's a family-run café in Heaton, not far away from me, that sells great cakes, not that I want to appear greedy, but it might be nice to show him I'm not a fussy eater or difficult to please. Listen to me! I'm now talking about a piece of bloody cake I may or may not have. I am going mad. Now I can't sleep and need alcohol of some description.

March

Friday 1 March

Thank God for the Centre! So good to have something to take my mind off the stupid date! I volunteered to clean out a cupboard to distract myself and ended up scrubbing every shelf until it gleamed, such was my nervous energy. It was a change to have *any* energy so I will happily take the nervous variety if there is nothing else on offer.

Feeling tired so will hopefully sleep unaided.

Saturday 2 March

Shi-i-it! I have thrush. Not had that for years and years. Probably a result of too much alcohol — and stress. Oh joy, another embarrassing trip to the chemist. Once I had to go for 'Hitchifanni' as I called it — like a new Japanese character complete with a range of merchandise: stationery, jewellery and other accessories. There was a multi-till queue which I quickly scanned for potential embarrassment factor. Phew — only till number eight, out of a possible eight tills, was manned by a cute young boy. My turn came: 'Till number eight please,' AAARGGHH! Was virtually shaking with embarrassment but it was too late to back out and I had to do the walk of shame and ask for the stuff to cure 'Hitchifanni' (though I didn't use those actual words). Horroroso! Why on earth was it considered dangerous enough to be placed behind the bloody counter? I assume it was company policy created by a misogynist. Cringe factor one hundred plus.

Nowadays I go to a carefully researched, tiny, all-female staffed chemist but still have to scan the shop for neighbours, friends, or anyone whose child I have ever taught, or the child themselves who could be at least thirty-five by now with embarrassing health problems of their own. It's a minefield! Went to said chemist but could see price of thrush tablet — seven pounds thirty, and left shop. Need to be more careful with money so looked online for some alternative (aka cheaper) cures. Bought a tub of live yoghurt and ate it. Not sure how immediate the effects are supposed to be but no change so far. I remember doing the same as a student with no money and spending more on the yoghurt than the cost of a tablet.

Sunday 3 March

Decided to give the live yoghurt another shot before wasting my money as it might need a couple of days to take effect. I read that alcohol should be avoided so went for a long walk to try and tire myself out before bed.

Monday 4 March

No green shoots of recovery in the thrush department. Running out of time fast. Resumed web search at first light for a more drastic, weird but interesting measure. GARLIC! No, not ingested this time: inserted! Hmm… sounds strange but I know that garlic has great healing properties, allegedly; these things are never proven. I am giving it a go. Had to wrap a couple of peeled cloves in gauze, like a vaginal bouquet garni and put it — well yes, up *there*. Couldn't see it doing much good like that so I crushed the garlic to make it more garlicky. I took that remedy and made it my own… ingenious methinks! Could market the 'crushed' bit and make a fortune! Puts a new meaning on, 'Would you like garlic in it?' Things are literally looking up.

Tuesday 5 March: date day or the day I went off garlic FOR LIFE!

Oh my God. Eff eff eff. Can't believe what happened. Doubt there's any way I will ever forget this incident but in case I'm lucky enough to have my self-preservation gene kick in and obliterate the whole, awful debacle from my memory, I may need to record the details in the diary.

Started with a shower and removed the specially adapted alternative remedy — now *off* the market for reasons of public dignity. Pooh — eau de garlic! Showered then seemed okay and garlic-free. Got ready for coffee date two. From what I remember he looked quite inoffensive: tall, hair on head not face, a bit nervous. Chit-chat reasonably interesting, had worked on Guardian etcetera blah, blah, none of it matters now. *Then* I whiffed it; a hint at first, but seemed to get stronger and more pungent by the second. Frigging GARLIC! Couldn't concentrate on anything he said after that and felt I had to say, 'Sorry I had garlic last night,' *had* being the operative word. Said a few feeble things whilst the smell escaped through my jeans at a rate of knots, pervading the air around me and Mr Journo. Shi-i-iiiit!!

Then came the very worst part... he suddenly remarked, 'You must have eaten a lot of it. What did you have, was it curry? I like a good curry.' Rumbled. All I could think is, 'He knows! He knows. He knows it's being emitted from my front bottom and is about to say, 'You should never have crushed it.'' I stared at him mindlessly and eventually succeeded in squeaking out the witty retort, 'Yes.' After that I *think* he reeled off a list of his favourite curry haunts, which the optimists among us may have interpreted as a hint for the next date, but more likely it was to divert attention from the vile stench of the invisible garlic cloud that enveloped us both.

In a state of blind panic, I leapt up saying, 'I'm so sorry, I don't feel very well. Must have been the curry.' The logic being that he would hopefully think they must have been garlic farts — not necessarily better than vaginal garlic but infinitely more normal. And that was the end of that. I walked all the way home as I couldn't risk being in an enclosed public space at any time in the foreseeable future. God, how long will it last? Even now I can smell it faintly.

That's the very worst experience I've had since I went to the doc's as a student with thrush — you couldn't buy any cure for it over the counter so you had no choice. It was always an embarrassing experience because there were very few women GPs in ye olden dayes *and* they were all about your granddad's age. I explained that I had thrush so he asked when I had last had 'intercourse' — cringe! I replied that it was about four weeks ago. Then, like something belonging in a sitcom, the receptionist burst in to report, in a very loud, stage whisper, 'You're coming through on the intercom in the waiting room,' WHAT? I then had the pleasure of yet another vaginal health-related walk of shame back through the packed waiting room to the exit. Aaaaaargh! Could see them thinking either, 'Shameless hussy, having sex before marriage. Serves you right!' or 'Ah four weeks since you last did it? Poor girl!'

Shi-i-iit. He was nice, Mr Ian Journo, I think. I came across as both mentally and physically ill. Right now he'll be telling his friends all about 'mad garlic woman' and they'll taunt him for weeks to come. Suppose I'm both. Frigging hippy remedies. And I've still got thrush.

Thursday 7 March: two days later and seven pounds thirty poorer

Now I've told everyone about the garlic experience. Had to share it (not the *actual* garlic) with someone or I would have gone mad. Then I thought, to hell with it, might as well tell them because they'll all get to know sooner or later. Of course, they think it's the funniest blind date story anyone's ever told them and that I *must* send it to Sara Millican or some other comedian to use as material in their show. No thanks. Don't want that thrust down my throat (though it would have been safer down there than in the other place) every time I turn on the TV after nine o'clock. Even Hilary laughed, but I suspect that was *at* me, rather than *with* me — I can assure you that there wasn't even a titter from me. Not sure I managed a smile. Oh no, the laughing-about-it-one-day stage is a very long way off indeed. Try me in the next millennium.

4.00 a.m. Can't sleep, though I am exhausted. My brain won't switch off, but it's all about trivia and how I hate Twat, with his smarmy bribery and money to burn. It's not full of work stuff — I don't work — or how to find a cure for cancer like scientists might be thinking at four in the morning, or anything at all worthy of thought. It's full of rubbish and nonsense and negativity. Having a brandy. I bought some in case it was better than the vodka. Feel like I am going mad but I don't know what to do about it. It's something I've experienced before and I'm at a loss. It's like being out of my depth with life. I'm scared.

Friday 8 March

For the first time ever, I had to ring in sick to the Centre. Feel dreadful for letting them down but I physically couldn't get out of bed in time. Couldn't face going in later either, I was so exhausted. Hope they don't think I'm unreliable and going off the volunteering. Nothing could be further from the truth.

Saturday 9 March

Forcing myself to write the diary but there's nothing to say. Been in a bad sleeping cycle so I'm getting up ridiculously late, feeling shattered and spending all day not doing anything except looking forward to going back to bed again. I can't shake myself out of it. Been ignoring emails from friends asking me to go out but CBA to reply. They will ditch me soon — a bad friend who doesn't respond to offers of help — why bother with her? Might be that SAD you get in the winter. Perhaps I will be fine in a few weeks and emerge, like an animal coming out of hibernation, rejuvenated by the sunlight in spring. Can't imagine that happening, somehow.

Sunday 10 March

Found it impossible to get up when the alarm went off, despite having four snoozes, then I fell asleep and woke up embarrassingly late. I felt worthless and angry with myself for being so weak. Sam rang — didn't answer the first three times, but she persisted and left messages threatening to come round if I didn't call back. At the end of our conversation she announced, 'Mum, I'm taking you to the doctor.' Not having the energy for a fight, I went along with it. Expect they'll tell me to 'pull myself together' and 'get a life'.

Sam duly called round shortly afterwards, ordered me to get dressed and practically frogmarched me out of the house to Exhibition Park. Bless her. On one of her precious days off she shouldn't have to worry about crazy mother and her wellbeing. I'm sure there will be plenty of time for that in the future when I am genuinely and legitimately infirm and in need. Not now, when she should be out enjoying herself and all I'm suffering from is a touch of the winter blues. The park was full of shiny happy people having fun, as

Michael Stipe from R.E.M. would have noted, with irony. I resented them, feeding the ducks and greedy swans. I used to love doing that but it's not the same on your own. Lovely Sam must have read my mind as we watched them and said she'd bring some bird seed next time.

Monday 11 March

3.00 a.m. Up again! I'm nervous about going to the doc's today. They will tell me to do exercise and get a routine (like a baby) so I can sleep like a normal person. I accidently looked in the mirror and nearly died of fright. Thought, 'WHO IS THAT? It surely can't be me. There must be some mistake. That *thing* is not me!' Had to have brandy for medicinal porpoises: a dose of dolphins? See. I have not yet fully lost my sense of humour, it just feels like it most of the time.

11.00 p.m. Sam rang at nine this morning to say she'd made me an appointment for ten o'clock. Talked her out of coming with me by putting on an extra-chirpy voice — that was an effort, I can assure you. Managed to prise myself out of bed and trowelled on a load of make-up to hide the dark shadows and bags under my eyes. In spite of my initial scepticism, the appointment was half-foul and half-not.

Rather than sneer and tell me not to waste her valuable time in future, the doctor took it all very seriously and suggested tests for the 'm' word — the bloody *menopause*! That was the foul part. Please, God, no. Don't do that to me. Not on top of everything else crap in my life. However, she appeared to take my reckless body clock and lack of energy seriously. She gave me a questionnaire to fill in and listened politely while I ranted a bit about Twat. It came out accidentally; I couldn't help it. She gave me some mild sleep-inducing anti-depressant pills. Suppose that was the good part. That means I must be depressed (not-so-good part).

This is the first time in my life that I've been given antidepressants. I know it's a very common condition suffered by many more people than you would expect, because people don't talk openly enough about it, but it feels strange hearing it about yourself for the first time. I wasn't even depressed when Twat left, or after the divorce, or when I found out that he *was* — surprise, surprise — seeing someone else all along. Back then I had my job and my self-esteem to keep me going. Ironically, stressful though it was, I could switch off at work. It was a welcome distraction without one millisecond spare to wallow in self-pity. I was needed by the kids at school, part of a team. Now I'm not needed by anyone.

Called in at the Centre on the way back from the doc's. I wanted to show them that I still exist and, in spite of my actions, very much need to volunteer there. Lucas noticed that I looked like a bag of poo, 'Are you well, Lizzie?' gave it away. He pronounces it 'Leezie' which I find so endearing. It sort of cancelled out the subtext of, 'My God you look rough!' Told him I was feeling rather tired and in his eyes I detected a look of disbelief mixed with genuine concern. It was very touching. I am blushing at the thought now, or having a hot flush thingy. Stop! No I am *not* menopausal! He knew damn well there was more to it but I reminded myself that I was there to assist with his needs, not the other way round.

Tuesday 12 March

Up in the night again. Doc said the tablets would work 'quicker than most but not immediately' whatever that means. I shall try to be patient.

Been reading about the 'm' word on the internet: 'Can feel like symptoms of depression,' was one. Now I feel even more depressed! One list of symptoms had thirty bloody four items on it including 'Disrupted sleep patterns' and

'Mood swings'. Now I'm confused! They needn't have bothered listing them all, could have written, 'Anything foul' and had done with it. In at number eight — cue the music charts theme tune — is 'Hair loss' whilst 'Incontinence' slips down two places (as it would) to number fourteen. I wish I hadn't looked. After all, the doctor will let me know once they have done the witchcrafty tests to check out the state of the old hag's eggs: have they shrivelled up and died yet or not? Joy of joys, bring it all on at once, why don't you? I'm convinced my skin is itchy (number twenty-two) today and my nails are most definitely more brittle (number eighteen). Sam told me not to be silly as it wouldn't come on overnight and that all I need is a good sleep.

'Avoid alcoholic drink' preach the tablets, so I had a very *modest,* English pub measure of brandy.

Wednesday 13 March

Simon called today. Must have got wind of the fact that the mad, menopausal, fast-becoming-alcoholic no-hoper who used to be his friend, has now been officially diagnosed with something and is not merely a grumpy old fart. He is insisting on a night out. Made myself do a big supermarket shop and even included some vegetables in amongst the ready meals I have become accustomed to existing on. Baby steps: it's a start, a good sign. Felt seriously knackered afterwards, though. Took the tablets with a tiny brandy ie English pub measure. Progress I suppose!

Thursday 14 March

I slept! Hallelujah, and if there is a Lord I shall praise him heartily! I feel like a new woman. Those little round bottled beauties are either placebos or go perfectly with a wee dram of brandy! The world is a better place by far today. I even looked a little less like something out of Macbeth when I got up. Unfortunately, the bags haven't been packed up and removed — they remain very much in situ under my eyes. Need to look for a remedy. 'Hags and Bags' — a catchy, if not attractive name for my new non-surgical cosmetic surgery business.

Cinema with Simon. Is he trying to finish me off (not in a nice way) and put me out of my misery? Another bloody subtitled film, of the 'films-to-slit-your-wrists-to' genre. No wonder he didn't tell me what it was until I agreed to go. God, men — even gay men — sometimes have no idea. Of course his ulterior motive was to interrogate me about the flaming dating site. Told him I was in no fit state for any of that malarkey and not remotely interested in getting saddled with another Twat, which of course they all will be.

Slightly nervous about not having brandy tonight but I am giving it a go.

Friday 15 March

10.00 a.m. Slept again! It's weird. Don't feel a hundred percent or anywhere near back to normal, whatever that may be, but I feel so much better for sleeping. Rang Centre to arrange to go in tomorrow instead of today. I'm not quite ready for it but need to do something. Occurred to me that I hadn't been to Pilates for ages so I forced my reluctant and dubious self to go. Wasn't too bad after all, as not many of the beautifuls were there. Maybe they were working, with it being a daytime class. It made a refreshing change not to be the only person in the room who remembers the Green Goddess and Jane Fonda's Workout. Found it harder than before although it's hardly what you could call proper, hard-core exercise. I'm not doing enough.

Hopefully will feel more motivated from now on, unless the anti-depressants make me even more lethargic and put on between five and ten stone. Can't afford to do that — still hanging on to Christmas fat which has usually been zapped way before this time of year. Also can't imagine having any *less* energy than I have at this present moment, but I do feel better for having done something, thanks to Joe P. and his successfully marketed exercise idea.

Saturday 16 March

Suspicious of the tablets now; they are too good to be true! I am sleeping, I am definitely a teeny weeny bit calmer and, best side effect of all, haven't thought about Twat for over two days. That's bound to change when Sam pitches up in her brand spanking new Mini (said the real, depressed me). Hmm... maybe the tablets aren't so good. Next time I will ask for ones that don't allow you to think *at all*. I could eat, drink and sit, content with my own company, never having to leave the house to attend Pilates again or feel guilty about not going. In fact it's quite an alluring prospect. Except I wouldn't be able to order food and drink deliveries if I couldn't think; I would have to go into a home with other people and that sort of defeats the object. Probably won't do that then.

I made it to the Centre today! It feels like I haven't been properly for ages, having missed a few shifts with the 'goings on'. I can see Les Dawson doing the face he used when talking about women's problems. He might have called it the 'doings'. Great to be back. The volunteers had coordinated a cook-in with funds raised from a car boot sale and we took a few people to the multicultural grocery shops to buy some ingredients for their traditional dishes. It produced spectacular results! Everyone helped each other and a splendid feast from every continent — okay excluding Australia or Antarctica as they're not home to yer *traditional* asylum seekers — was created. I had to rush back to the house and knock up a shepherd's pie which was an effort, not simply to make the damn thing but also to think of something British and presentable, apart from chicken tikka masala of course. It was worth the effort. Lasagne, pizza and chilli were all dismissed on grounds of origin although they, like those who brought them here, are an integral part of our culture. Even the Gordon Ramsay shepherd's pie contains rosemary (not a native herb) and garlic (aaargh!) otherwise it would taste like dog food and everyone would hate it.

I loved seeing Minika laugh again. She was in her element, ordering all the men about, most of whom had clearly never learned to cook in their own countries. It was like watching the great Gordon himself, except without the swearing. Lucas, on the other hand, produced a fabulous chicken casserole with sweetcorn, capers and plantain, refusing offers of help along the way.

The authorities are dealing with his case. He can't write letters or send emails to his friends and family for fear of them being intercepted, then he'd be traced. If that were to happen, the recipients could be tortured, or worse, as retribution. Imagine, it's as if you no longer exist. Your identity is lost, obliterated in one fell swoop. Okay you — time to start a whole new life from now! To some, that may sound appealing, but to have it thrust upon you is an entirely different matter. Lucas — though I now realise that can't be his real name — says that if he is allowed to stay he will nevertheless return one day to his home country. Like Pablo Neruda, the exiled Chilean poet, he will return when it is safe for him to do so and not before.

Wish I could increase my days at the Centre, it's the highlight of my week. Sadly they don't encourage it because they find people suffer from burnout if they do too much, then disappear altogether. They said they'd be flexible with the days if I wasn't well. Perhaps they think I am seriously ill, or are able to see that I'm struggling. It was kind of them. Now my eyes are filling up — a positive sign; a familiar emotion is making its presence felt. I am on the road to recovery, or at least approaching the slip-road leading onto it with caution.

Sunday 17 March

Hilary rang to see how I was doing. I suspect Sam et al of filling her in on the gory details because her tone at the start was one of immense and uncharacteristic concern, as though she was talking to a recently bereaved person. Then I told her I was a lot better and certainly feeling more like myself so she asked, in all seriousness, if I had arranged to meet up with Dave One again! For frig's sake, Hilary! That woman is unbelievable and with less of a clue than me! I didn't dare to remind her of garlicgate date or she would probably call him on my behalf. I wanted to scream at her, 'LOOK — I feel like I have been through a mangle *then* spun dry for good measure. Strange as it may seem, Hilary, the LAST thing on my mind as I was reaching for the anti-depressants was,'Now then, I must hurry up and get better so that I can set myself up for another ludicrous failure in finding a man!" Knowing her, the reply would have probably been, 'Is that a 'yes' then?' God, she knows how to test drive those bloody tablets to their limits. Don't think Lewis Hamilton could have done a better job.

Monday 18 March

Heard someone say, 'He was effin' and jeffin'. Fantastic! I LOVE that expression. Now, everyone, conjugate the verb 'to jeff'!

Tuesday 19 March

Computer is on the blink. Tried banging on the top of the modem thingy like Dad used to do with the TV, which worked a treat in the 1970s but strangely enough you don't get the same response from a computer. They are fickle, new-fangled beasts. Sam is good with technology — I will ask her to call round. Twat used to do all that sort of thing. Serves me right for not asking him to show me what to do, though I expect he would have avoided showing me anyway, control freak that he was. He loved to think he had the upper hand. What did I ever see in him?

Pleased to note that I am slightly less angry — albeit a miniscule amount less — than I was a few weeks ago. Could be down to tiredness of course…time will tell. We shall also see if The Verve were correct when they proclaimed that the drugs *don't* work and not only that but they actually make you *worse* — which would be massively annoying.

Wednesday 20 March

Awoke without an alarm to a lovely sunny morning. I was almost appreciative of it and, dare I say it, *motivated* to go out for a walk by myself along the Quayside. Hooray! At last! I adore the bridges and there's nothing like a bright morning down there with the silvery river shimmering in the beautiful winter-into-spring sunshine. Listen to me, waxing lyrical (don't mention bloody waxing, it's not summer yet).

Went to a café where two young women, student types, were meeting. The only clue to the casual observer that they may be even remotely acquainted was that one was waiting by the door for the other to arrive and they hugged before sitting at a table, getting their phones out and remaining silent for the next twenty minutes. I exaggerate — one said, poshly, 'Was Hugo out last night?' to which the reply was, 'Yah,' before resuming the real business of chatting on social media sites, no doubt, to anyone else except the friend they were purportedly meeting for coffee. I watched the people watching their screens, possibly watching other people, possibly not. Great if you're alone and self-conscious — I confess to checking my phone twice for texts, but that was all.

Young single people be warned: you will never meet a potential partner in a café — you will be too busy staring into the virtual world of your screen instead of the real world that surrounds you, full of real people. Perhaps I am doing you a disservice and you are staring at real people on your dating site. Be careful with that route also, they may lie about their age.

Thursday 21 March

Sam called me and asked, in as casual a voice as she could muster, if I'd checked the dating site or had any emails from them. I snapped a reply, in an effort to shame her into silence: something about being mentally ill and wishing everyone would keep their noses out, then felt guilty and apologised. Then I checked the site — what a hypocrite! Worse still is that someone who will have to be known as Dave Two (I knew there'd be another one along soon) has emailed me! Disaster. I didn't open it — not *that* much of a hypocrite — might open it tomorrow. I obviously *am* a fully blown hypocrite.

Friday 22 March

Opened email before I left for the Centre! I mean, come on, it's like having a parcel or a letter sitting right in front of you on the kitchen table with a big label attached saying 'Open Me'. I am a mere mortal. Annoyingly, he seems rather good on paper:

psychiatric nurse — caring, special people, often a bit whacky
good-looking on photo — been fooled by that one before
fifty-eight — probably means sixty-two

similar interests including politics — hmm, sounding too good to be true.

Told Sam, (mistake) so now the torture has started. Drip, drip, drip. 'When are you going to reply? No time like the present. What have you got to lose? What else would you be doing on a Tuesday, Wednesday, Thursday?' etcetera, etcetera. I retaliated with weak and feeble excuses: 'Shopping, washing, reading, housework,' which were mostly lies, stopped short of, 'Cooking,' as that would be pure fiction. She knows I will crack in the end. There's so little in my life at the moment. Must do something about it. Though I am definitely better than I was, 1 don't yet have the energy or inclination for anything — if truth be told. The whole process is utterly alien to me; I feel like my body has been invaded by another life form — an appropriate choice of words as I feel like I'm on another planet most of the time. For my daughter, and a peaceful life, I agreed to reply. Might email him tomorrow; will check him out in the virtual boreometer. Sigh... here we go again.

Saturday 23 March

Looked up 'having your lip lines lasered' — nice alliteration, should do it if only for that. They're the ones I got from whistling and definitely not smoking, which was years ago. No, mine are from whistling. People usually think it must be an old man whistling when they hear me. I try not to these days, on account of the lines and the cost of the lasering. 'Lasering — lotsa lolly!' Sounds good but won't exactly attract the clients.

Sunday 24 March

Emailed Dave Two.

Tuesday 26 March

Announcement: those tablets are damn good! I am sleeping normally, without any assistance from my trusted friend, brandy, who is now demoted to acquaintance and relegated to the back of the cupboard, out of sight, for now. Despite a few worries and anxious thoughts whirring around my brain when I first get into bed, they are swiftly dealt with by the drugs, I expect. It's like one of those fly-killing machines they have in hot countries — buzzing around happily one minute then you hear the tell-tale 'zap' as the machine puts a stop to their fun with the magic of electricity.

Main news: Dave Two replied! I'd asked a few things about his job, travel and music interests this time, instead of my previous approach of not wasting time, which proved to be a grave error. His answers to my questions were very amusing so can maybe conclude that Dave Two is witty! Okay cynics, he might have got a friend to compose them for him. He also asked lots of questions about me — all good so far. Emailed back, possibly a bit too keen, but I was semi-restrained; stopped short of suggesting we meet up. Tried to dazzle him with ready wit and repartee of my own — ho ho. Feeling secretly excited about this — am I losing my judgement? Perhaps the drugs are too strong or maybe I've been beaten into submission by the boredom and frustration of my current life — difficult to tell. Whatever the reason, I can cope with it.

Wednesday 27 March

Simon came round and asked, well demanded, to see Dave Two's emails. The cheek of it! Word travels fast on the Sam/Sara grapevine. Felt strangely disloyal showing him. I mean, what if this the start of something deep and meaningful? If so, I've shared our first ever exchanges with gob-on-a-stick Simon! Might as well have a print run of a thousand done and hand them out on Northumberland Street on a Saturday. I could add an account of garlicgate onto the end for good measure. That said, he thought it all very exciting. He reckons Dave Two sounds suitable and looks 'fit — for an older man'. Cheeky monkey that he is! The man's a mere three years older than me. Must face facts, I am now an 'older woman', clinging on by her fingertips to the forty-five to fifty-five bracket on surveys and questionnaires. Ugh!

Thought about joining the gym again.

Thursday 28 March

MEETING DAVE TWO ON SATURDAY! He asked me first! Shi-i-iiit! Going to a café in the Haymarket. At least it's busy so I can always people-watch if bored, though it is too bright in there. Must remember to sit with back to window if it's sunny, or even if it's not.

I still have Christmas fat! Might join the gym I left a few years ago when work took over my life and I hadn't the time to go. Went to Pilates — God, the young crowd there are so bloody rude. There were five of us there, four young'uns and moi, but they didn't include me in any of their general conversation during the breaks. It's not as though they're all good friends; they're all young and I'm not. End of. Scarcely made eye contact with me. Our teacher, bless her, was lovely and kept asking me things in an effort to be inclusive but the other lot didn't. Was I like that in my twenties? I can't remember — would like to think not, but from what I've seen I think I may well have been.

Wonder if HRT is still being dished out like sweets — hope so because I think I had a hot flush again earlier, or was it a side-effect of reading Dave Two's email, for the twentieth time?

Friday 29 March

All interested parties i.e. all of my friends and family, have now been notified about the date, or I would have been in big trouble! Every last one of them has texted or emailed to say, 'No garlic for tea!' Not funny or original, you lot. It's still officially too early to see the funny side of that one. Had a strange sensation today and couldn't put my finger on it at first, then it dawned on me: excitement! I remember those days but they are by no means recent. I am happy to play host to such a positive emotion once again. I am not sure how long my guest will stay, but I am enjoying their visit while it lasts.

Might join the gym tomorrow before the date, then I can tell him I am a member of a gym. In the meantime I've bought some overpriced miracle-working skin cream; an irrational act of a depressed woman or a sound investment? Time will tell, although I only have two days including today.

Centre for the afternoon. Tempted to spread my news about Dave Two but stopped myself — don't want to:

a) jinx it

b) appear desperate

c) admit to getting him from the online dating site — call me old fashioned. 'Hi you must be Old Fashioned.' 'Yes, call me Old, most people do.'

Lucas wasn't there. He had a meeting with a lawyer provided by the Centre to help him through his refugee status application. I missed chatting to him.

Tonight I tried on almost every item of clothing in my possession in an endeavour to combine attractive, casual, tasteful, and un-frumpy with made-an-effort-but-not-too-anxious-to-please. Failed abysmally. Eventually enlisted help of Sara — Sam being too brutally honest for such a task. I'm too fragile for brutal honesty at this moment in time. Finally came up with something that makes me look vaguely fit for purpose. Had to raid the cupboard for a Spanish measure of vodka and a brandy chaser to calm the nerves, despite taking my medication — hence illegible scribble. No garlic ingested in any way, shape or form.

Saturday 30 March

D.D.D. — Dave Date Day
Well! That was brilliant! He looked like his photo, but even more attractive, was interesting and interested in me! Reminded me very slightly of Alan Shearer when he had hair, an older version of course, no disrespect to Alan. We used to frequent the same clubs and pubs when we were students (Stage Door, Tuxedo Princess aka The Boat, Whiskey Jar, Free Trade, Ship) so we had plenty of shared memories to talk about. Time flew. Could have stayed in that café for hours, reminiscing. Not sure how it could have gone better. Partner left him three years ago (a few months after Twat left me). One slight niggle: partner was forty-two... hmm. Maybe he's now after a safer pair of hands — so to speak! Listen to me getting ahead of myself or 'giddy' as Gran would have said. It's a welcome relief to feel something towards another man that isn't hatred and loathing. Spent the afternoon and evening basking in a rare state of contentment and calm. Makes a change from feeling gloomy and worrying about anything and everything. No alcohol required tonight and I'm still pretty giddy.

Sunday 31 March

The best Sunday I've had for a long time! Spent most of it reporting back to: Sam, Sara, Simon, Hilary, and even Chris and Debs who I haven't spoken to for ages but we email fairly regularly. In fact, once they knew there was online dating in the offing they were both bombarding the inbox for more details! Didn't mind the third degree this time as I loved reliving the moment. Naturally they're all asking if I'm seeing him again so had to re-enact the dialogue word for word:

Me *(bravely)*: Let's do this again sometime.

Him *(enthusiastically)*: Yes, definitely! I'll email you.

Great excitement all round. I need to calm down. He hasn't emailed but I wouldn't have expected that to happen so soon! Trying to keep cool but it's not easy in my condition! Needed relaxation music, candles and wine to properly wind down before bed.

Should go back to the gym to get rid of my new-found nervous energy, and the Christmas fat of course. Put extra dollops of the miracle face cream on. That should help matters. Must make sure next date isn't somewhere too light. Might dig out some recipe books (if I can find them) or even look online and make myself something interesting which doesn't involve the piercing of a film lid. Can't believe I'm having such unusual urges. No, not *those* sort of urges — boring, domesticated ones.

April

Monday 1 April

STILL NO EMAIL! I'm not April fooling you either — checked it around fifty times today — must get a grip. Tried going to the shops and (unbelievably) doing *housework* to take my mind off Dave Two and his lack of communication. Now that's what I call desperation! I had to be curt with everyone who asked if I'd heard anything, as it was getting right on my nerves. As if I *wouldn't* be broadcasting it if I did hear. Then they give you those irritating platitudes like, 'Weeell, it's only been a couple of days now, he's probably trying not to look too keen, playing it cool to keep you interested,' ad infinitum.

Two days is nothing, *nothing* in the grand scheme of things. Don't want another bloody relationship anyway. I'm going to call it a friendship from now on. I thoroughly enjoyed his company, that's all… and his lovely face.

Tuesday 2 April

Day three of no email.
More of the same: checking, checking, checking. A watched inbox never bears fruit. That's my twenty-first and nineteenth century combo. It's true though — a cool persona needs to look genuine so I am staying positive… ish. Asked about re-joining the gym. If I am to compete with the forty-two-year-old, the body needs to comply.

Ate thousands of biscuits by way of compensation, for everything.

Wednesday 3 April

Day four of no email.

Still no bloody email. Sara said that if she was genuinely cool and interested she'd leave it a week. A WEEK? I'll be a bag of shredded nerves by then. And fat. But I am holding on to that thought. Must stop eating the biscuits. Went for a short walk around the park. Too late to pay the gym membership by the time I'd remembered.

Accidentally looked in the mirror and caught sight of my roots, mainly too dark but then some frighteningly *white* ones! I am going grey on top of everything else. Didn't want to investigate further so I've no idea of the extent of it. Will avoid looking next time.

Thursday 4 April

Ditto yesterday.
Holding off on gym enrolment in case it's not necessary. Sam says I mustn't worry, that it'll be fine and assures me five days is nothing in the casual stakes. She is the queen of casual, that's for sure — but you can afford to be casual when you are an early-twentysomething with absolutely everything going for you! Wondering whether to ignore her and email the philanderer. Someone talk me out of it, please! But hold on a little minute here, we are grown-ups after all, too old for playing games. We are open, honest, sensible people who ought to express how we feel and act accordingly and in this case I feel like emailing him. Now!

No, I've just looked at the time; emailing at eleven thirty at night smacks of the alcohol talking or desperation. But I am getting desperate — am I actually admitting to that? Will hopefully read this back one day in the Shady Pines care home with my memory box and think to myself, 'God how bloody pathetic! Did I never grow up?' Then someone will say, 'Time for your medication, Lizzie.'

Friday 5 April

And on the sixth day…
Did it. Not first thing, I exercised restraint and waited until after I'd been to the Centre. Yes, I am stupid. Stop yelling, 'WHAT HAPPENED TO TREAT 'EM MEAN, KEEP 'EM KEEN?!' from the sanctuary of Shady Pines — you're not me now! Sam said in a tone of voice that betrayed bitter disappointment, usually directed at children who have let down their parent or teacher, 'Oh Mum…' Sara responded with, 'Okay,' which went up at the end, as if lost for sufficiently tactful words upon hearing such a dreadful confession. But they will eat those words, every last one of them, when I get the reply saying he's been working night shifts and how hectic it's all been and that is why he hasn't had a minute to reply. Yes, he's probably on a late shift right now and won't have checked his email. That's what it'll be.

Saturday 6 April

Day seven — not a day of rest at all.
Quite the contrary! A day of crap and angst. Full of self-loathing about how pathetic this is/I am. It's like being a teenager again without any of the positives i.e. trapped in the body of a fifty-five-year-old woman. If it were the other way round it would be ideal: I'd be all-knowing and ultra-sensible yet young and fun-loving at the same time, except there's nothing at all sensible about this fifty-five-year-old, so the teenager would be no better off. Time to sleep, if I can.

Monday 8 April

Day nine.

Hideous hangover all day. Feeling wretched. What possessed me to do that? I have gained nothing and lost a day. For what? For a bloody man? Why did I let myself get into that state when I was doing so well before and feeling like I was on the up. A salutary life-lesson: follow your gut reaction. When someone says, 'Why not try online dating?' and you feel physically sick at the thought, *it's for a reason.*

Day eight was when I received the measured reply, aka the bombshell, to my email:

Hi Lizzie

It was very nice to meet you last week. (*NICE? Exactly how much more lukewarm can you get?*) Unfortunately I have too many commitments at the moment and won't be able to meet up. I wish you the best of luck and happiness in your retirement and I hope you find someone to share it with.

Take care

Dave (*aka Patronising Twat*)

So there you have it. Each word will have been agonised over, deleted, retyped, deleted, replaced then he would have gone away and looked at it later, making sure there was nothing ambiguous for me or my over-enthusiastic friends to cling on to. Had he left it at, 'I won't be able to meet up', they would have said, 'Oh he means 'at the moment,' blah, blah, bloody blah!' The message was well and truly sledge-hammered home (with one of those used by builders for knocking down walls) by the last sentence — should she be left in any doubt. I must appear more desperate than I really am. And I know exactly what the 'other commitments' will be... a younger woman from the bloody 2gether dot friggingcom. 2bloody fussy more like. If he's used to the fortysomething he won't want to downgrade to the arse end of fifty. Twat. Who does he think he is? Don't think Alan Shearer would act so, well... so irresponsibly! GRRR! And he's made me 'grr' again. Anyhow, he had a few stray eyebrow hairs.

The remainder of yesterday was spent eating junk food then started on the Spanish measures early doors — *in*doors actually. Felt FOUL today. How could I have been so stupid? What on earth would he see in me? The very, very, very worst part is the fact that he clearly thinks I'm desperate; I must have oozed desperation from every middle-aged pore in my sad old body. Grrr! Desperately seeking: anyone. I wanted to reply, telling him it was never my idea in the first place, I was railroaded into it by my friends (I've got hundreds, you see) and that I am perfectly happy on my own, it's just that I need more to fill my days with and by 'more' I do NOT mean *men*.

And another thing, Dave Two (you are ten a penny) I can't help it if: my job was all-consuming and I had no time for my past hobbies and interests; Twat felt neglected and left me and my retirement plans — ah diddums, poor neglected man. I decided against it, as that could be misconstrued (or *con*strued) as mad and semi-stalking behaviour. 'Semi' because it would only be the once but he would be terrified of it blossoming into a fully blown stalk.

Utterly drained now.

Tuesday 9 April

A day of reporting back, or rather, asked Sam to contact every interested party under the sun to save my embarrassment. Went to town alone to see the Matisse Exhibition — fantastic. Walked along the river. Stopped at the café with my book for a while. Beautiful and sunny outside. Felt calmer but still miserable, a dull ache inside; I am mourning my lost dignity. I know it's a common or garden knock-back, but it's one I could have done without at this point.

Resorted to my trusty ol' mate brandy again tonight. Becoming adept at writing when partially drunk.

Wednesday 10 April

Haven't done much. Not slept well, despite the medicinal alcohol. Had to get up in the night and have another brandy so not sure if that counts as strictly medicinal or whether we are now straying into the realms of alcoholism here. Must DO more and stop dwelling on the rubbish that's going round and round in my head! That, I'm afraid, is easier said than done.

Just when I thought this week couldn't get any worse, I remembered the hospital appointment tomorrow — UGH! Now I definitely won't get any sleep.

Thursday 11 April

Before Christmas an invitation arrived. How exciting! No, it was an invitation to a bowel screening mmm... lovely. However, because invitations of any sort are few and far between these days, it still counts. The bottom line is (couldn't resist that one) it was fine and anyone who is lucky enough to receive a similar invitation must not be in fear of the procedure.

The wonderfully professional staff talked to me non-stop throughout, so I was denied the luxury of being nervous and wondering when it would all end. In fact, by far the most embarrassing part was beforehand, when one of the team asked me if I was travelling anywhere by plane in the next few weeks. Taking this as the nurse's equivalent of a hairdresser's, 'Going anywhere nice for your holidays?' and not wanting to appear like the sad person I am, without plans to go anywhere or do anything at all, I replied, 'No, but I might go away in July for a weekend with my daughter somewhere up the coast, or maybe the Lake District.' I then elaborated further about Sam not having much time off work blah blah and more blah. After answering, 'Oh that's nice,' in a rather bemused tone, she then explained that, had I been flying soon, they wouldn't be able to perform the screening due to the potential risk of changes in cabin pressure. I felt such an idiot!

Afterwards I sloped off, hoping I hadn't held up the queue with my unnecessary, long, bogus holiday plan explanation and farted my way home through Exhibition Park.

Friday 12 April

Centre today — very mixed: great to be feeling like a semi-useful member of society for the day, but terribly sad. A memorial was held for Jakub. There were photos of him and people fondly recalled the times they had shared with him, and how unbelievably cheerful he was for a boy from such a traumatic background. They laughed about how he was the master of practical jokes — harmless, childlike pranks such as filling the salt cellars with pepper, hiding the contents of the food cupboard and replacing them with silly notes saying 'Yum-yum!' and 'Help us, we've been kidnapped and we're about to be eaten!' All the while he would lie in wait, eager to see the look on the volunteers' faces, then collapse into hysterics, his infectious laughter permeating the place like a ray of sunshine, adding sparkle to the day.

Now he's dead. Murdered. I just can't bring myself to think about it. How could we have allowed that to happen?

Monday 15 April

I've been a recluse. Fobbed off Sam and Hilary with, 'I need to go into town,' lies. Couldn't face either of them, one being too upbeat and the other too depressing. I'm starting to dislike myself intensely. Stayed in, despite the company being dire. Drank both nights (awful). Watched crap TV (good). Forced myself to eat. No energy. This is *not me*! I feel like a different person, but not in a good way like the expression would imply. Thought I was doing so well. Maybe I'm immune to the tablets. Might go back to the doctor and complain. Worrying about the menopause now after waking up in the night, sweating. Charming! I truly can't cope with that now. Hilary said it was, 'Probably all the bloody alcohol pouring out of your skin'. She does have a knack of saying the right thing now and again, bless her, and I think I needed to hear that. Harsh but fair.

Tuesday 16 April

Worries:
future
money
health — including mental wellbeing and m-word
alcohol and all the diseases it causes – NEVER google 'alcohol-related illnesses' unless you want to be fished out of the nearest river
Easter weekend — a long bank holiday looms ahead

Thursday 18 April

Interesting how the way you feel about different times of year can change drastically according to your circumstances. I loved the build-up to Easter when I was teaching — a change of routine, arty crafty activities, cards, decorated eggs, Easter nests — some edible and some utterly inedible. The younger children, wildly excited about the arrival of the Easter Bunny to the point that the threat of him *not* coming was used by parents and teachers as a most effective disciplinary tool, akin to Santa Claus at Christmas. Two non-existent characters who wield more power over your kids than you could ever achieve…impressive! And I would always get at least one Easter egg from Twat or Sam or a child at school. Now I view it as an ordeal to battle through — another family-orientated holiday second only to Christmas in its awfulness, sent by God to remind depressed, bereaved, divorced and any unhappily single people of how lonely and 'unnatural' it is to be on your own. The majority of my single friends are very happy (particularly the divorced ones!) but there are a few who aren't and occasions such as these serve to rub their noses in it — and mine at the moment.

Town was quiet. I walked around it aimlessly. Even the flower stall lady at the top of Northumberland Street had thrown in the towel due to lack of custom. The students, conspicuous by their absence, have finished for Easter. Must go and use the local Tesco while I can walk down the aisles without the need for a cattle prod. Didn't speak to or email anyone today. Bring on the long Good Friday.

Good Friday 19 April

Sam called round this morning bearing gifts: a huge Easter egg and flowers! That girl is such a sweetheart. She's super-excited about Ben, a new bloke at work who she's very keen on. In fact, I don't think she talked about anything else, which was fine as it kept her off the subject of her mother who has clearly lost the will to live and ignores any advice proffered by her daughter! She did her therapy-by-the-back-door routine i.e. got mother out of the house by saying, 'I fancy going over to the park.' Until this year, the last time Sam expressed a desire to go anywhere near the park was when she was six, and now it's her number one venue of choice, not that I'm complaining — it was good to get out. It felt like a Sunday: shops shut, park full. At least things will be more normal tomorrow, except for me, that is.

Easter Saturday 20 April

Now I think, technically speaking, that you're supposed to be sad on Easter Saturday because Jesus died yesterday, but everything in town is open again and everyone looks reasonably happy to me. In fact, when I went to Asda, the staff were in hysterics, running up and down having egg and spoon races! It was very jolly and cheered me up no end.

Called in at the Centre to see if they needed any help due to the Easter hols and volunteers being away, but they were okay. The new guy, Lucas, waved and shouted, 'Leezie!' at me as he was rushing out of the building, which was very sweet. Had a chat with Minika, always a most humbling experience. She's one tough cookie, bounces back after any difficulty, and I mean *any*. You learn that that these people have suffered so appallingly in their lives that everything else is now relative. Whilst another person would possibly need counselling after being assaulted on a bus, Minika regarded it as a minor irritation.

Went to bed with a feeling of dread and nausea. Panicking about the day ahead and the bank holiday nonsense. Sara texted to see if I wanted to go out for lunch at one of the riverside pubs or the Ouseburn. Very thoughtful of her! I love my friends. Ungratefully, I feel I can't face it: the happy families enjoying their lives, or perhaps feeling rather fraught themselves at the prospect of another two weeks of entertaining the kids, *and* the weather forecast is bad. Can't justifiably refuse on those wimpy grounds ... what would Sam have to say about it? And what else will I do? Hilary will be spending time with her family. Deadly boring though they are, at least she has grandchildren to keep her occupied during the dark days of an Easter weekend. Hopefully won't have to listen to the stories of how wonderful it was. God, I'm so nasty — a fully-fledged bitter and twisted middle-aged woman.

Easter Sunday 21 April

What a great day! One positive about having depression is that you can be pleasantly surprised every so often when a good time unexpectedly jumps up and slaps you in the face, in a friendly, non-aggressive way. I imagine those people who are born pessimists, or rather, brought up as pessimists by their parents, must never experience the emotion of disappointment and are occasionally taken aback by actually having fun.

Sara had a little treat in store for us first: taxied to a bar, an old haunt of mine from the 80s, used to be The Newcastle Arms, where there is a hidden gem — a roof terrace with a spectacular view over the river! She knows me so well; I'm a sucker for a roof terrace! What's more, it's right under the Tyne Bridge and every brick, stone and girder is steeped in the history surrounding it. The first bridge over the Tyne was built in Roman times — suppose they had to have some means of transporting the parties of stags and hens to the Quayside clubs for the weekend!

Walked along the river — sun shining, water sparkling, people smiling. Yes, even I was one of them. I love to see tourists here. Makes me proud to think that we live in a place other people want to visit! If the weather's bad and I see tourists around, it evokes pangs of guilt, as if I am personally responsible for both the rain and their happiness. I always hope they're not wishing they hadn't bothered to come. At The Tyne pub we enjoyed live music and a barbeque — perfect. Then up to the Free Trade — everyone's favourite, traditional pub with a beer garden offering unrivalled views of the river and its impressive selection of bridges. Always a hit with the visitors.

Admittedly it sounds like a pub crawl, but I was sensible for a change, paced myself and ate along the way. I feel so much better for going out and my spiteful fears about the happy family brigade were unfounded due to carefully chosen venues, engineered by lovely Sara who behaved impeccably by not mentioning the 'm' word ('men' without the 'opause'). Although she went into great detail about her own latest exploits: seeing two men, Tom and Chris, at once, neither of whom knows about the other. 'Both are casual so they have no right to complain,' she declared! Said it was all going fine until Chatty Bob, a guy she knows from the Collingwood pub who was doing some work for her in the house, saw Tom leaving one morning and Chris arriving for tea a few hours later! Sara being Sara felt compelled to explain the situation and asked him not to mention anything to either of them about any other man being there! She'd had to share her darkest secret with Chatty Bob, who would be bound to put his foot in it at some point. After all, he ain't called Chatty Bob for nothing! She made him swear to secrecy as the pub is where she and Tom, but not Chris, are regulars. I loved hearing the tale and can't wait for the next instalment entitled: 'Chatty Bob has one too many and blabs.' Thank God those days are over for me. I can't picture having one, let alone two suitors on the go!

Bank Holiday Monday 22 April

I have survived the long bank holiday — if I can make it through to the end of the day. Just the evening to go now and can honestly say, if I dare, that I've enjoyed it thanks to my marvellous daughter and fabulous friends. Had a text from Simon asking if I wanted to come for a drink at the coast. I've been positively inundated with requests now! It's uplifting, but I had to decline on the grounds of preserving my liver — and not in the pickling sense of the word. Stayed at home and ate chocolate eggs instead. Mmm... much healthier.

Tuesday 23 April

Been on the post-Easter choc-fest-binge diet. It's great —
might market it! Ate tons and tons of the stuff in an effort to
divert my attention from the opened bottle of wine in the
fridge. Now feel guilty about the chocolate. What's this hate
campaign against sugar all about? I was brought up on
adverts telling you in no uncertain terms thatyou *must* eat a
chocolate bar every day in order to function *at all*, or else
you would faint through lack of energy then probably die.
As a result we were practically force-fed chocolate and any
sweets containing mega amounts of sugar. I remember
seeing 'research' by 'scientists' who lectured us on the
importance of sugar for our general well-being. This
dubious research turned out to be sponsored by guess
who... yes, the sugar refining companies! But I'm sticking
with those evil sugar-peddling pushers (not to be confused
with 'pedal pushers', the innocent trousers) and I am
prepared to believe every last word of it.

Could I be getting my sense of humour back now? No.
Not really. Pulled out a few grey hairs then gave up on that
particular losing battle. I have plenty more I ought to be
fighting.

Thursday 25 April

Now trying to abstain from the temptress known as
'chocolate'. Apparently it increases the urge for alcohol.
You *cannot* win. Also been reading about women who pile
on so much weight on anti-depressants and can no longer
get out of the front door unaided so now I'm doing double
damage, or treble with the alcohol. God, life is so dull once
you start playing by the rules.

Need to get out more — I know I keep saying that but I
must remind myself in the hope that one day it may finally
sink in. Doing things costs money, though. Going out to

places costs money; money that he should have given me. I will have to investigate free days out for grumpy middle-aged people. Wonder if there's a club for the likes of us — come and join the 'Misery Mob: we specialise in wallowing in self-pity. It's a laugh a minute!' I suppose I could always start one. On second thoughts the last thing I need is a new group of equally dysfunctional friends.

Friday 26 April

Centre for half the day as had doc's appointment. Says I'm right at the very start of the m-word. I'd better not beg for HRT quite yet. Besides, after the conversation we had about the symptoms not adversely affecting my life, she declared, 'There's no need for immediate action.' Ooh brilliant, that means I can carry on doing absolutely zilch with my life and say it's doctor's orders! Somehow I don't think she'd agree. I *stupidly* mentioned my evening/night time drinking. She asked if I thought it was a problem. No it's no problem drinking, it's stopping that's the problem — boom boom! Now it'll be in my notes that I have a drink problem. Stupid idiot for mentioning it. Big mouth.

Came home and had a couple of English measures of vodka. Very restrained. Move along please everyone, no drink problem to see here.

Saturday 27 April

Night Out with Sara
I knew it was mistake before I went. It was the night before last but wasn't in any fit state to write yesterday as felt so miserable and wretched due to thumping hangover that I simply couldn't BA. Even the magic potion I discovered in the corner shop couldn't shift that one. I started taking it when the nice lady said, 'All the young lads are buying them.' Sold — to the middle-aged woman with the drink

problem. A tiny bottle of something mysterious and pink, for ninety-nine pence labelled simply 'Tonic'. Had to be worth a shot. I now swear by them, but only for a mild dose of the hung-overs. Let's face it, nothing bar an early night (or hair of the dog) can cure a mega-hanga.

Poor Sara. She was trying her best to help an old friend in need, but it was another total bloody disaster from start to finish. Tried on everything I had and decided on something with a high-heeled accompaniment: mistake numero uno. Immediately felt teetery-tottery therefore vulnerable and ridiculous. At times, Sara forgets that she is much younger than I am, which is usually most flattering but on this occasion an appalling oversight on her part. We taxied into town to a bar where groups of twenty-to-thirtysomethings congregate. I comfortably qualified for the title of 'the oldest swinger in toon', or at least in that room. Refused to go to the bar in case they wanted to see my ID, declare me too ancient for the image of the place, and forcibly eject me.

Sara dragged me tottering along from bar to bar, feeling every bit like her mum. Every last one of the men in various arrays: gangs, pairs, individuals, were staring at Sara like she was some celebrity or rather, an *object,* yet she didn't even notice. Must be so used to it by now but I found it uncomfortable, irritating, and damn rude: objectification of women. You don't get gangs of women staring at men like that, their tongues practically hanging out. Grrrr! Queues of baying, chanting men outside the strip clubs, the lap dancing clubs with their newer names: 'table dancing' or 'gentleman's' clubs in a pathetic attempt to give them an air of respectability and mask what's actually going on inside. How has it come to this? We didn't fight sexism tooth and nail, hand-to-hand combat in the eighties to get back to *this*! 'Ah,' they tell me, 'you have no sense of humour. It's all done in the name of irony and it is you who is at fault because everyone knows that men and women are now equal in all aspects of society including all matters sexual, so what's your problem, woman?' Rant over.

The ultimate humiliation of the evening came when we were minding our own business in a relatively quiet bar and two blokes decided they would impose on our evening with the sole intention of spoiling it. One was a tall, loud, ski-tanned, brash type in a suit, showing off a ridiculously oversized (like his mouth) watch. Big watch small penis? Luckily I was denied the opportunity to test that theory. Had hair-transplant-type hair. The other was quiet, dull, bald, trailing reluctantly along behind, knowing his place; the boss or rich friend calling the shots. Clearly they had struck a deal whereby the flashy gobshite could chat up Sara whilst the other one was most likely instructed to bore me (the mother) to death, possibly spurred on by the promise of a trip to the lap dancing club if he complied. The dead eyes and disinterested face before me betrayed all. Adding to their utter gall was the fact that they were both much nearer my age than Sara's and she had absolutely no interest in her admirer. She always prefers younger men. The sheer arrogance of it!

After what felt like hours, I heard Flash Harry inviting us back to their hotel bar, so that he could entice Sara back to his suite of rooms when things got 'a little more interesting', no doubt. Bollocks. I caught her glance, pleading for me to help out so I jumped up before she could answer and barked, 'No thanks. Bye.' Outside, Sara laughed and laughed, thinking it was hilarious that I didn't even make an excuse or say, 'Thanks, it's been nice talking to you.' But why would I? They were bloody rude enough to impose on our evening uninvited. Didn't even ask, 'Do you mind if we join you?' a rhetorical question often posed as they are squash themselves into the seat next to you, without waiting for a reply.

Many a time in the dim and distant past I've said, 'Yes, actually, we do mind. We're having a conversation,' resulting in some sarky comment or, on occasions, verbal abuse to cover their embarrassment of rejection. Still, it was always better than having to feign interest in a load of unsolicited drivel from strangers, meanwhile planning your escape. If they were worth talking to then they would have appeared slightly embarrassed when tentatively asking to join us.

Sam particularly enjoys my stories of when I was her age in a club and, if a guy asked me to dance, I would sometimes say, 'If I wanted to dance, I would be dancing.' Cool as anything, although I would usually save it for the arrogant ones who never expected a knock-back.

Sunday 28 April

Spent at least half a day on the internet. Doing what? NOTHING! Shady Pines people, pray tell me: does the internet still exist or have they given up on it as a time-wasting device getting in the way of work, leisure and life in general? I'm joking! It helps me to pass the time, which is a bonus these days. What else would I be doing?

Monday 29 April

I have raised my daughter well. That has been proved to me yet again. Another fact is that I am reeling from the other night and have zero tolerance for sexist men. Sam and I were walking into town for coffee on her half day off when, from a building site, came cat-calling and a shout of, 'Oi! Gorgeous!' Needless to say it was not directed at me, but before I had a chance to verbally savage them, Sam had crossed the street and approached them. Through the wire mesh the conversation went something like this:
Sam (with a serious face): Yes? What do you want?
Builder: Ooh now you're asking!
At which point I get worried that it may all backfire, but no.

Sam: No, seriously, you called me over so what exactly do you want?

Builders all look at the protagonist and giggle. He looks at feet and can't think of an answer, turns around and shuffles away followed by jeering mates who can see that he has been thwarted.

Sam: Pathetic

That's ma girl! She was impressive. Possibly felt supported by my presence, could be a gamble on your own i.e. will the others all turn on you in defence of their mate, a men versus women thing? She told me how sick she was of feeling intimidated and harassed by that sort of behaviour when walking alone down the street in the middle of the day, minding her own business, not seeking attention from men. I said that she should encourage all of her friends to do the same. That would soon stop the ogling sexist prats. I'm indescribably proud of her.

I told her about my friend Chris who, whenever possible, would make a note of the firm's name and call them to complain — it was very effective. One person she called told her that it was company policy *not* to call out to passing women, and that if people didn't report it they would be unaware that it remained a problem. At least that doesn't happen to me now. Hooray! I've found a positive about being a fiftysomething!

Tuesday 30 April

Another new month looms. I am gearing up to more volunteering. Tomorrow I will make an effort. If I can commit it to paper, I might commit to it in reality.

May

Wednesday 1 May

Charity Shop from Hell

A new month, almost summer. May Day, traditionally Labour Day. I did some work in honour of the occasion, or at least *arranged* some. I am trying my hardest to be proactive. Asked at the various animal charity shops if they need volunteers but they don't. Pity. Twat not only didn't *like* animals but was also conveniently allergic to cats, dogs and horses so I could never have one single pet, apart from fish and I don't count them. Fish are not pettable. I hated him more for that. I will get a cat when the time is right. Perhaps that should be sooner rather than later, after all I have eschewed any plans to go away on holiday. I love the word 'eschewed'. It sounds like you spat the idea right out of your mind.

So … I went into the mental health charity shop (close to my heart at the moment) where they were advertising for volunteers and was shown around by Gloria, a self-important woman who found it much too difficult to smile. During the tour she barked some questions about how much I wanted to do and did I have any experience of working in charity shops, to which I was tempted to reply, 'Yes. I've built a successful career out of working in a charity shop.' Instead I decided on, 'No.' I received my orders that I was free to go and agreed to return tomorrow when I would be allocated the task of 'sorting', whatever that may entail.

Unsure about all of this but telling myself not to be so negative. She might not even be there tomorrow. Definitely need a couple of drinks if I'm ever going to sleep tonight.

Thursday 2 May

First and Last Day at the Charity Shop
NEVER work in a charity shop! Well, not that one, anyway.
I'm sure the animal ones would have been lovely and
cuddly and fluffy, unlike this one. Maybe Gloria (badly
named by her parents) has mental health issues herself
which may explain why she acted in such a *hideous* manner.
Either that or she'd been kicked out of the army for bullying
all the other sergeant majors, or perhaps forcibly retired
from the prison service for being too harsh. Wouldn't be
surprised if she was a bouncer who'd been 'let go' for
brutalising the punters in a club up the west end, frequented
by gangsters. No. Absolutely nothing would surprise me
about that terrifying woman.

Gave myself a good talking to beforehand and arrived in
a positive frame of mind, feeling relatively enthusiastic, to
find myself ushered into a windowless room aka a cell at
the back of the shop with June, one of Gloria's 'cluckers'.
They're a little group of 'yes' women, clucking around her,
asking permission to do this or permission to do that, or
permission to breathe. Each one was petrified of her. June
showed me the art of 'sorting': some items, good enough to
sell, were all to be washed; some items, unfit to sell were
destined for the 'rag-bag' (no, not Gloria). Then I was
escorted to a washing machine and shown how to use it but,
before we had the chance to load it, Gloria pounced on the
clothing, snapping, 'I need to check it.' So, not even June
was deemed skilled enough to decide what would sell and
what wouldn't. Having passed the test, she then raked
through the rag-bag and pulled out an ancient, faded yellow
jumper. 'That'll do for someone!' she declared. 'It's
marked,' I said. WELL — how *dare* I question The
Empress! I thought June was going to have an attack of the
vapours, Jane Austen novel style, and have to be
administered smelling salts as she was almost shaking at the

thought of confrontation. Gloria fixed me with an American bald eagle-like stare and addressed me as though I were:

dirt
a child
a dirty child

I would never speak to any child in such a way. She sneered, 'What?' which was a rhetorical question as she knew damn well what I'd said. So I went for it, '*I said,* it's marked.' June began twittering away in the background, saying something about trying to remove the mark and how it might come out in the wash, chirp, chirp, chirp. Then, like one of the protagonists in *The Third Reich: Rise and Fall*, Gloria snapped, 'June, PUT IT IN THE WASH!'

That was enough for me. I could see how the place was ruled with a rod of iron and not in a tight ship kind of way — this was a fully blown *dictator*ship! I was silent for the rest of the day. She thought she'd cracked me. Truth is, I didn't dare open my mouth again for fear of a terrible tirade of abuse tumbling from it, scaring the poor, nervous, clucking dears to death. They told me I'd be allowed to sort, then eventually price,the bric-a-brac, books and household goods, but that Gloria priced all clothing. Evidently this is a skill too complex and valuable to be undertaken by a lesser mortal. I completed my shift, or rather, endured the rest of the day alternating between watching the clock and watching Gloria who, when she wasn't barking orders at the cluckers, was terrorising the customers! 'No you *can't* have it for a pound less. The price is as it says on the label and that goes for everything!' 'Can you put that back the right way around?' Customer replies, bewildered, 'Sorry?' 'The hanger — TURN IT AROUND! IT DOESN'T GO THAT WAY!' Customer begins fumbling with hanger which is then snatched from hand by Gloria's talons, snapping, 'Give it here!' The cluckers looked at their feet or busied themselves with imaginary jobs, as minions do when the dictator loses their temper before bludgeoning one of them to death for giving them too many peas. I simply stared in disbelief thinking, 'Mental health charity? This will tip me over the edge for sure.'

I'd had all day to plan my parting speech. I knew I'd never forgive myself if I didn't say something to this dreadful woman. It ranged from one line to about three pages. In the end I settled on a couple of sentences. After thanking June and the others (whose names escape me) for their help, I turned to the po-faced Gloria, my stomach churning, and said, 'I won't be back next week. In fact, as long as you're here, bullying these poor women and hounding the customers out of the door, I shall not set foot in the place.'

She stood, open-mouthed and scowling as I did the Long March with jelly legs, to the door, by which time she'd had enough time to regroup and, in a slightly less snappy voice than earlier, quipped, 'And don't come back!' Well, I suppose she had to have the last word, ridiculous though it sounded under the circumstances.

Got home and poured myself a brandy.

Friday 3 May

Ashamed to admit that I called in sick at the Centre again. I know it would have made me feel better to have gone but I was far too weary. I didn't even get dressed. I have never done that in my entire life. Think I'm suffering from the awful night out at the weekend. Trying desperately not to think about it as it depresses me more. I know what I ought to be doing but somehow can't make that last step and motivate myself into action. Watched daytime TV — always a bad idea, no better than the last time I watched it. Trash. All absolute trash. On principle, I refused to watch what some people call 'modern day bear-baiting', where dysfunctional, struggling families tear each other apart to the whoops and hollers of the audience and, undoubtedly, many of the viewers at home. Instead, I whiled away the hours with the now familiar programmes about people unearthing stuff from their loft and selling it for a lot less than they expected. Greedy people buying houses at auction, sometimes repossessed by the bank from unfortunate owners who'd lost their jobs and could no longer pay the mortgage, although they don't tell you that side of it as it spoils the ambience for the happy viewer. Then the prospective buyers would get a quote from a builder, evidently out of his comfort zone in front of a camera, unsure of where to look, whilst the presenter mediated and calculated as the final profit was revealed, leaving the buyers salivating and wringing their hands with glee. However, a house would sometimes be sold to another buyer, way above the featured buyers' budget, rendering one entire half of a programme a complete waste of everyone's time. Cue the viewers, including myself, jeering spitefully from our sofas as the pound signs fade from the now not-so-smug, unsuccessful buyers' eyes.

Chat shows: innocent but full of rubbish; soaps and sitcoms; cooking galore! Produce a gourmet meal for six out of the three things lurking at the back of your fridge (including cat food) one of which is always the dreaded garlic. Still can't bear the smell after garlicgate, and I adored it before. My dish would have to be 'rubbery old carrot and onion in goose fat', left over from the days when I could be faffed to have people round and make a roast dinner. Sadly, those days feel like a lifetime away.

Saturday 4 May

CBA to write much in diary tonight. Who in their right mind (which I'm not) would want to read about misery? Certainly not the residents of Shady Pines — it would most likely finish them off. The most annoying thing is, I felt much better a few weeks ago. In fact, I was convinced I was better, completely better. Cured, just like that. A magic wand of medication, a little help from my friends and hey presto — no more depression! Apparently this is normal for the condition or illness or whatever label you choose to attach to it – 'the menace' more like. I must try harder. I could write out one hundred lines of: 'I must try harder' and see if that works. The Victorians used to swear by it. However, I don't think I could BA.

Sunday 5 May

A perfectly LUSH day! Possibly subliminally influenced by daytime TV, my positively herculean efforts to do some de-cluttering of the loft paid off as I discovered a hidden treasure within: my box of old diaries! Warning, diary readers and diary writers... there should be rules for writing a diary and here they are:

Do *not* write in code — you will never ever remember what or who the initials stand for. Instead, make sure you hide the damn diary properly!

Include lots of detail, especially if it's a funny story as you will appreciate it later.

When including an in-joke or hilarious anecdote, do *not* simply write the punchline, expecting, thirty plus years later, that your ageing, perimenopausal brain will step up to the mark and fill in the missing essential details, or you will have wasted your precious time, energy, and the world's resources.

I shall illustrate each point with a corresponding example:

Went to HT's for C+D then back with BH and 2 CTs.

LUSH LUSH time with PW at H's.

Dog saying, 'It's so weird!!!!'

What does it all mean? I can guarantee that it will remain a mystery. Nevertheless, it sounds like we were having fun! It brought a smile to my miserable face and evoked happy memories of a time when life was about having the maximum amount of enjoyment while telling your parents the minimum amount of truth; the latter being a prerequisite of the former. A time when we were anything but invisible, longing to be older and taken more seriously. A time of lists, endless lists! Not your organisational 'to-do', functional variety, oh no — the, 'Let's make a list for the sake of making a list,' category of list. For example:

People you've snogged — could take hours depending on how old we were at the time.

People you'd like to snog.

People you've slept with — later in life.

Then there were the shared lists, i.e. those who both or all parties involved had snogged or slept with. There were joint lists of boys you all agreed were: the most *and* least fanciable aka lush; the funniest *and* most boring; the nicest *and* nastiest. All of the above would then have to be placed in rank order thus prompting hours of debate and hilarity as we argued and cringed about each other's preferences,

'No he *can't* be number three, he was deadly boring and totally unfunny!'

'Yes but he was pretty,'

'Okay but I still think three is far too generous for him!'

There were the lists of real people in imaginary situations. These would cause the most 'laughing till you can't breathe' situations and take up entire evenings as the scenarios became more and more ridiculous. Prefaced by, 'Out of ...' you knew what was coming next when one of us would choose between two and four of the least attractive, boring or lecherous blokes you could think of and force the others to choose which one you would sleep with for example: if you were shipwrecked on a desert island; after the plague had killed everyone else; if you were locked in Eldon Square shopping centre for the night and had to do it to keep warm. Sometimes they would be politicians or celebrities but more often than not, and much more fun, were people we knew from the least attractive list: friends' brothers, teachers or anyone equally inappropriate you could think of to make us all squirm. There was no wriggling out of it, you *had* to choose or order them. Saying, 'None of the above', was simply not an option. It was against the law. As with the lists, after everyone had made their choice, each one would again be debated upon and, unlike a group of men discussing women, which would most likely be based on looks alone, that is when the most interesting and amusing discussion would ensue. More laughing till you can't breathe; the benchmark of a good night — in or out.

Can't remember when I last laughed like that. I must have done, but it feels like a very long time ago. I need to revive the 'Out of ...' game. Maybe I'll try it out on Hilary some time.

Bank Holiday Monday 6 May

Couldn't resist picking up the diaries again. They've cheered me up and kept me distracted from dark thoughts about Twat, today being a bank holiday, and the general malaise of the world. Had a lucky find: one of the first ones I flicked through landed open in the middle of the Menorca story, aged twenty-three. Uncle John's favourite of all our anecdotes!

Uncle John was my godfather whose wife died shortly before he retired. Without a family of his own, he used to join us for family birthdays and Christmas. He would remind us about the sorry tale at least three times a year. So, for once, the diary wasn't necessary. Admittedly I had conveniently placed it on a shelf somewhere, deep in the dungeons of my memory. You'll see why I store it there, dear diary readers. What could possibly be so dreadful, I hear you ask? If you are sitting comfortably in your reclining chair with adjustable footstool, I shall enlighten you:

My great friend Chris and I went on a grown-up hotel holiday to Menorca for a week. Discovering the local disco — no clubs in those days — as a source of possible holiday romance, we thought we'd give it a go. A fairly attractive, slightly older bloke crashed in on our evening. In those days we were rather less confident than we were in our late twenties when we would tell them to get lost. So, like the rat that he was, the conman could smell an easy touch a mile off. He leeched onto us, ordering rounds of drinks and asking us both to dance with him, thereby scuppering any chance of us sampling the local talent. At the end of the very long and rather dreary night, la cuenta was ordered and … he disappeared! The end. Yes, leaving us with the whole enormous drinks bill! We were apoplectic with rage; no diary needed to recall that feeling! Feminists though we were, insistent on paying our way and splitting bills when out on a date, we didn't want to pay for the lothario too! Taken for a right ride, we were. Mugs, even at that young age, ooh now I can feel myself getting radgey again.

Must try to cling on to the positive thoughts gleaned from the funny side of the diary stories and not think about Twat.

Tuesday 7 May

A great day after a shaky start. Dreamed about Twat. YUK. Why, oh why does the human mind play such terrible tricks on us? We were still together (nightmare) holidaying happily on some island location. How could that be? I was enjoying my favourite pastime, snorkelling amongst the most exquisite fish and colourful coral in cool turquoise waters — my idea of absolute heaven, then I woke up. I woke up to reality. To the sound of raucous, taunting laughter from my subconscious. I could almost see the tiny, red cartoon devil, complete with trident, thrusting at my brain, punishing me for something in a former life or for being a miserable cow in this one. Shook him off, though, by getting up and rummaging through the diary box.

Found a great one: Debs and I, in sixth form, acting out the school dinner (calling it 'lunch' was considered affected). This was a ritual which you may well be tempted to reinstate in Shady Pines to while away the hours between mealtimes; I can thoroughly recommend it. Being the least mature sixth formers Gossingforth High had ever encountered, we used to charge around, giggling, smuggling younger friends into the coveted sixth form common room for a dare to see how long it would take before they were turfed out. One of us would stand at the foot of the stairs, below the blackboard which displayed the menu, and mime — a la charades — the dinner choices whilst the other, stationed at the top of the stairs, attempted to guess the day's culinary delights. Over the months, a code was developed — similar to the process of repeatedly completing cryptic crosswords. So, due to the lack of variety in the 1970s school menu, it would take mere seconds to crack and therefore became slightly less fun. That said, a ritual wouldn't be a ritual if it were performed only occasionally, or abandoned after a few stints. The Massai tribespeople didn't say, 'Oh this dance is now boring because everyone knows what's going to happen next. Let's think up some new and exciting moves that no one will recognise,' or it wouldn't be a ritual! Thus, the dinners had to be acted out for the entire final year of sixth form.

The Code

Sausages became 'rah-rah-rahs', uttered as a growl like the Yorkshire Terrier from *That's Life* who, snarling through bared teeth, very vaguely sounded like it was half saying, 'Sausages'. Yorkshire pudding, as you can imagine, became mixed in with the 'sausages' dog mime; not to be confused with sausage dog because that's a different breed altogether.

Mince (at least once every week): a camp walk, and dumplings: obvious isn't it? Peas: pees — again uproariously funny. Chicken: easy. Custard: particularly foul (back to chicken) but funny, nonetheless, to us — 'sounds like...' mime squeezing a spot (pus) then mime doing a poo (turd). Simple! Jelly: lots of jiggling about — funny for the passers-by and 'eye-scream': seeing how loud you could scream and get away with it. Being immature *and* exhibitionists, we secretly relished an audience. Although the stairs traffic could obstruct the mime, a crowd would often gather and join in the guessing but it would inevitably escalate, the participants becoming giddy and attracting the attention of prowling teachers or pink-coats aka dinner ladies, to give them their proper 1970s title. It was best carried out during our free periods, when the occasional teacher would pass, smile and shake their head, questioning the calibre of the current sixth form intake, lamenting the decline of standards, and pondering on how much further they were likely to fall.

Went to bed happy tonight, after enjoying a microwaved lasagne with broccoli, wondering how we would have done that one, had there been such exotic delicacies on the school dinner menu!

Wednesday 8 May

Well, it's either the diaries or the drugs or a combination of the two, but my mood is definitely lighter and the cloud is fast becoming a paler shade of grey — about thirty, if fifty is the lightest. On a DIY superstore colour chart it would probably be called 'Mid Steel'; somewhere between 'John Major' and 'Wood Pigeon'. I ought to be going out more but at least I'm enjoying reminiscing — instead of watching bloody daytime TV.
Bad Taste Disco

Unearthed another sixth form anecdote from the chest of treasures! With ourselves being the obvious exception who did nothing else but, people at our school were too cool or sensible to deign to make fools of themselves. This point is perhaps best illustrated by the 'Bad Taste Disco' fiasco and anything else that ends in 'sco', apart from the large supermarket chain who had nothing to do with it.

Debs and I trawled the charity shops and jumble sales (now a rarity, reinvented as a car boot sale) in a quest to find the very worst clothing imaginable. Some of those fabrics and even the exact items have come in and out of fashion since, but were very much *out* at the time of the said disco! I ended up with a nylon, very blousy blouse, printed all over with green parrots, and coupled it with a bright pink taffeta knee length skirt that stuck out in all the wrong places. Finished off with some clashing yellow tights, I was right royally proud of my efforts! Debs chose a full length 60s ball gown that was too short for her, with the worst ever swirly wallpapery carpety design on it in orange, purple and green. She did a great job with clumpy shoes and hideous jewellery and together we looked a complete sight! Enhanced by strictly clashing lippy and way too much Miners eyeshadow, we set off for the ball looking like Cinderella's sisters.

I can remember even more of these details, not recorded in the diary, because of what happened when we walked through the school hall doors. At first we weren't quite sure if we'd got the right night, like arriving at a fancy dress party when you're the only one who's dressed up. And to make matters worse, you've come as a bloody Smurf so no hope of anyone wanting to snog you — Smurfs are definitely *not* snoggable. EVERYONE else in the entire sixth form was wearing their own, fashionable clothing which very, very, very slightly, didn't quite match! They stared, laughed and said how great our outfits were and how hilarious we were — but they were undoubtedly, one hundred percent certainly going to get snogged and we weren't.

I can recall, even at that tender age, the feeling of exasperation — after the initial embarrassment — at their lack of imagination. Then again, not everyone is blessed with the innate sense of self-deprecation that we possessed. Reliving it all, I laughed and laughed, not quite until I couldn't breathe, but somewhere on that spectrum! What better way to end a day?

Thursday 9 May

Went out to eat with Simon in Chinatown, staying tactfully clear of all cinemas lest he be tempted to whisk me inside one which would put a stop to any green shoots of recovery I may have been experiencing lately. After the meal, he came back and insisted on seeing some of the diaries. Unsurprisingly, there wasn't much he could understand due to the encrypted nature of the tomes, but I showed him Bad Taste Disco and, as a bonus, managed to locate a similar experience, this time from my student days: Gnome Party. He started to read the first few words 'Gnome Party with D. Shite,' then it became illegible so I had to fill him in on the longhand version of the story — he loved it!

As the title suggests, Debs and I had been invited to a Gnome Party. Great! Again, we went to enormous lengths to look like real live, authentic gnomes, complete with cotton wool beards, red noses and fishing rods. When we arrived — yet again to our horror — it became evident that our female student counterparts had decided to interpret it as a Pixie Party and came sporting sweet little booties (trendy at the time) with maybe a touch of red lippy to unnecessarily enhance their already perfect cheeks, and pointed hats with little bells on just to add to their cuteness. Not another bearded lady in sight, neither natural nor otherwise. Once again, we had been duped. We entered into the spirit of the thing and paid the price, heavily. Everybody wants to snog a pixie. However, as would be the case with a Smurf, nobody wants to snog a gnome with a full cotton wool beard. Believe me, I know.

Friday 10 May

A very productive day — for me. The Centre staff are organising a ceilidh evening! Asked me for help with the food prep and selling tickets. Great! Can't wait to see the cultural mix. A ceilidh is always a laugh because no one knows what they're doing – except for a few elderly Irish or Scottish people. It'll be funnier still when they call out the moves to a roomful of people, many of whom have a rudimentary grasp of English. I wonder what they will make of, 'Dosey doe your partner,' or is that Country and Western? I am also clueless!

Emailed Sue and the old school staff. I can think of several who'd come. I also asked all of my old couply friends who weren't Twat's own original friends (only two were his, unsurprisingly) and of course my lovely current small but select crowd. Must ask Sam and Ben, who is mentioned in every conversation I've had with her lately. It will be a good test to see if he comes. Might get myself into town to buy something new to wear for it. Show willing. Unsurprisingly, I haven't been since the sausage-skin-swimsuit escapade so I'll have to psyche myself up first.

Saturday 11 May

What has happened to the shops? I didn't take it all in when I went to buy the sausage suit for the dreaded spa day as I was on a tunnel-visioned mission. Since then I have had no reason to go into town to buy clothes. Arguably, a blind date may be deemed as a perfectly good motive to warrant a purchasing trip, but I was in no frame of mind to make any sort of effort then (CBA mode).

I learned some horrible home truths today: the shops I used to frequent do not stock one wearable item for me – I have grown out of my favourite shops! I am too old for them. Have they changed their target market or is it really *that* long since I last went out? Probably the latter. After raking around the old haunts I ended up in the pricey departments stores which were my last resort for something remotely suitable.

Clothes have shrunk! I was never, ever a fourteen. Now, some of the fourteens don't come near me. What's going on? They may well be skimping on the material to save pennies and increase their already vast profit margin, but it's poor marketing when your customers refuse to buy something on the grounds that there's a number sixteen on the label. Might start a business where the sizes are all generous (or wrong). 'Size Matters' could be our strapline. So in my shop I'd be a twelve or even a ten thus making women feel good about themselves – they'll flock in. Obviously all geared to the older lady who feels bad enough about her declining body without having the boot stuck in by going up a couple of sizes. I remember my mum saying, 'Ooh if I were twenty years younger, I'd buy that,' and I'd reply, 'Don't be silly, you should wear what you want. Don't let your age stop you!' But it does. Some things in those shops today looked ridiculous on me, but would be fantastic on Sam or even Sara, who's a thirtysomething. Mum probably thought, 'Just you wait…' and she was right.

Having fought my survival instinct which yelled, 'Quick, run away!' I regrouped (army speak) did breathing exercises and chanted, 'I shall overcome,' silently several times in my head. After at least four hours, when I almost cracked on more than one occasion, I persevered and finally found an inoffensive long tunic thing to wear over jeans. Mission accomplished.

Casualties: 0
Wounded: 1 – my pride.

Tuesday 14 May

I have created my own therapy, a new variety — free of charge: Diary Therapy. 'Diarpy'? No, it sounds like a mixture of diarrhoea and wee. Not a healing experience at all. I shall have to give it its full title. I might patent it, then the dragons from *Dragons' Den* can tell me that it's not worth the paper it's written on, make me suffer for ten excruciating minutes then declare, respectively, that they are 'out'.

Diary Therapy has a trifold structure:

1. Writing your diary is therapeutic in itself. It is cathartic. You release tension, anger, come to terms with things, reflect, and maybe make sense of your mad life.

2. Reading diaries from when you were young is (hopefully) very amusing. It reaches out to the fun-loving, carefree soul within that may not be quite as glowing as it was yesteryear, but still has the ability to inspire you.

3. For your dotage — no not now — for Shady Pines. For your memory box. People can read them to you. You may or may not remember the incidents or characters. You may not even recognise yourself, but others will learn about you, your life, your loves, your achievements and regrets; the real you, not the little old lady you. Your diary will serve as an aide-memoire for your entire memory! It may be genuine therapy. And it will come in very handy as an alternative pastime when you want to duck out of bloody chairobics.

Had I not tried it myself, I might have presumed it would be a rather depressing experience and make you want to recapture your youth, but I would have been wrong; it's great! I'm thoroughly enjoying reliving the funny and even cringing stories and am surprisingly calm and accepting of a new chapter emerging in my life. This chapter needs to be written, filled with events, fun, '*stuff*', even nonsense. Anything, for God's sake! Who wants to read about misery? I need to get a grip and start living again, with a zest for life, not merely because I wake up each day, not having died in the night, wondering how long the next twenty four hours will feel like and how on earth I am going to get through them. I had that zest, that joie de vivre at one time. It's true, I had it for most of my life until my fifties. Then the work stress kicked in, the marriage broke down, and I retired to nothing. Which is worse? Please choose from the following options:

Option 1: stress + no time
Option 2: too much time to fill + no energy

It's a tough call, that one. At the moment I would prefer Option 1. Then again, the grass is usually greener.
Definitely feeling better in the past few weeks than I did last month. There. I have ended the day on a positive note! By way of a reward, I may sleep well tonight... fingers crossed. Goodnight.

Friday 17 May

Great day at the Centre! Lucas is back from his trip to London and he told me about all the spectacular environments Colombia has to offer. It made me want to go there, until he revealed that some of the most beautiful parts could be unsafe for foreign tourists to travel around. Nevertheless, it sounds like the most diverse and fascinating country: rainforests with their wealth of hidden treasures, including the Amazon region on the border with Brazil and Peru; coastal areas for whale-watching and fantastic snorkelling; mountain villages where indigenous peoples live an almost self-contained life in traditional dress; beautiful beaches and tiny islands, some containing only one house; towns and cities with impressive colonial architecture, a pretty but salutary reminder of their brutal past — the plundering of gold and the enslavement of their people by the Spanish. Colombian people are as varied as the climate: a mixture of the indigenous population; those descending from the Spanish settlers; those of African origin whose ancestors were shipped in as slaves to work on the plantations.

With great sadness, he said that the most impoverished in society are those of African origin, although in some regions the indigenous people are also extremely marginalised. Apparently, the children at his school are very poor and he told me with pride about securing a grant from the British Council for one particularly able student to study English at university because her parents couldn't afford the fees. A passionate and committed, caring teacher — one who was prepared to go to prison for his principles. He talked about organising the strike, about how nervous his colleagues were but he had persuaded them that it was the only option left: they were on poverty wages with no prospect of a rise, negotiating and pleading had drawn a blank and, to top it all, prices had risen so much that it was no longer a living wage. I felt humbled. I told him how we had been on strike for pay in the seventies and a few times since then over pensions and workload, but we were never in any danger of being sent to prison for it.

He's such a lovely man. Discovered that he is slightly older than he looks: forty-five.

Saturday 18 May

Looked up an 'eye bag removal' thingy. I look at least sixty at the moment and boy do I feel it. Sara says I'm imagining things, bless her. Then I looked at the cost. No thank you.

To add insult to injury I was junk mailed yet again by bloody 'Silvers — Autumn Years' exclusively for the over fifties. My hair is NOT and never will be, SILVER! If I get ONE more thing from them I will go round there — wherever they live — and tie it to a brick (or use masking tape) and throw it through their Head Office window — and that's *after* six weeks of medication! On turning fifty, I made the dreadful mistake of seeing if they could offer any consolation for entering the misery of a new decade by providing cheap car or house insurance. Well, the answer was a resounding 'No,' but not only was it a total and utter waste of time and a phone call, they have junk mailed me ever since, despite my shoving them firmly and ritualistically back into the post box with 'PLEASE RETURN' on them. They keep on coming, on and on and on. 'Silvers' holidays. The joke of the fortysomethings, smugly too young to be eligible.

Why sit on a coach with a load of like-minded, i.e. similarly depressed, OAPs touring around every single one of the stately homes of the south east of England? It may surprise you, Silvers, that I DON'T want to see how the other half live, or used to live, when the rest of us were struggling to survive. Nor do I want to pay nine ninety-five for a cream tea in the claustrophobic café that sells memorabilia of the wretched place and anything quintessentially English: English tea, English honey from English bees (none of yer foreign bees here, madam), English flavoured shower gel and other smellies, anything made from roses e.g. air freshener, to give the impression you have rose-scented poo. Hey presto — if you fall in a barrel of the stuff, simply apply the spray to come up smelling of the proverbial! Yuk. Not sure which smell would be worse.

Tuesday 21 May

Spent most of the day trying to download music onto my phone. Allegedly easier than ye olde CDs and conveniently providing us with music on the go, but I beg to differ. Sam informed me later, when she came on an 'emergency callout', that I should have pressed, sorry — clicked on 'cancel' about the same number of times I clicked on 'accept' or 'ok' which is apparently how I got into a terrible mess. DAMN YOU, technology. I hate you!

Wednesday 22 May

Four people from school, Sam *and* Ben (one brownie point) then Hilary, Sara, Simon plus one — if they stay together that long — are all coming to the ceilidh! It's so lovely of them all to have rallied round to support me and the Centre. I love my friends! I'm hoping they don't still have that dance called 'The Gay Gordons' or Simon will think it's hilarious and be all extrovert and embarrassing. Oh well, it will add to the entertainment. Having my hair done for the occasion. Might even add a new colour to the highlights…why not? I'm on a roll!

Thursday 23 May

Was delivered a huge blow (not a blow *dry* or any other blow phrase) by my hairdresser, whom I very much liked until today. She told me I could no longer have my usual blond highlights, or any other coloured highlights, as there is now too much grey! What? No warning WHAM! No more highlights for you, Lizzie. Misery. Must admit that the all-over colour does look lovely, but I will miss my streaks of blonde and occasional smatterings of red if ever I was feeling adventurous.

Yet another ageing milestone. I need to keep calm. She also cut it nicely, in such a way that I no longer resemble Winnie the Witch's grandma on a bad hair day.

Friday 24 May

Centre. Minika was telling Michael about her experience at the Housing Office and how the woman's tone of voice changed from polite when dealing with the local man to downright rude and abrupt when it came to her. She wasn't angry, she was hurt. I, on the other hand, was FURIOUS and asked her if she wanted me to complain on her behalf but she virtually pleaded with me not to. Felt so protective of her. Michael told her how he was in a busy newsagent's in town with two people serving but without a queuing system. Tired of being ignored, he left the shop. No one seemed to notice. I want to march into that shop and shout, 'Listen! This man has suffered enough in his life without you ignorant idiots making him feel worse!' Don't think he'd appreciate the gesture, somehow, but I'd feel better. I nearly said, 'Well I've been speed dating so I know about suffering,' but that would be flippant and reduce their experience to some laughing matter, which it wasn't.

These days, when I'm out for a drink, I hate going to the bar because when (not *if*) I get overlooked for a younger customer I can't stop myself snarling, '*I* was next!' thus creating more tension as what was lack of thought (indifference again) escalates into hostility with the barperson starting to *resent* the no longer invisible stroppy middle-aged woman. Not sure which is worse. Grrr!

I left the Centre feeling a little more positive, having volunteered to help on a stall at the Unity Festival on Monday. It's a dreaded bank holiday so it's a relief to have a plan for the day and to feel useful — an added bonus.

Monday 27 May

Unity Festival
A celebration of diversity, created as a stand against right-wing groups who feel the need to beat their chests and flex their racist muscles on occasion, sullying our multicultural streets. By some miracle, the bank holiday weather was kind to us for once and the sun shone on our stall during my stint from one o'clock until three. Lucas came to help for an hour. We chatted a great deal about everything and nothing and I noticed how pleasant and obliging he is, treating everyone with the utmost respect. It was a fabulous day! From an early age, my mum told me there were 'bad men' hiding in the bushes of Leazes Park. Consequently, even as a rebellious teenager, I was terrified of going near the place job done, mum. Luckily these urban mythically bad men didn't extend their stomping ground to Exhibition Park — though I don't imagine that stomping is what they were allegedly all doing in the bushes (maybe due to insufficient bushes?) so I was never in fear of that park. Leazes Park is beautiful and never more so than today: people dancing, picnicking, soaking up the first rays of summer sunshine. People of all ages and cultures with a common aim — to support their city's variety of ethnic groups and have fun in the meantime. There were stages and music areas, colourful stalls, a myriad of community groups, charities, and unions — all on a smaller scale than the well-established Mela or Pride events later in the year.

As the afternoon drew on, a chubby young man from the St John's Ambulance group grew increasingly redder and hotter from running up and down with stewards directing ambulances here and there. I'm sure every festival has its collapsed teenager: a combination of crowds+heat+alcohol will always have consequences, but there was no sign of trouble — just an upbeat, positive vibe.

The organiser was spotted walking around with a donation bucket and a huge grin, like he'd become a father for the first time. He had indeed given birth to a successful event on this year's summer calendar; months of hard work having paid off. I walked home, fulfilled and contented — feelings that have eluded me recently.

Sam and Ben came for tea and we dissected the day. Early night due to mental exhaustion — 'too much excitement for one day' as my mum would have put it. And, to my great relief, I didn't see any bad men in the bushes.

Tuesday 28 May

Dipped into the diaries and coincidentally came across the time of 'Crazy Colours', when we all had pink, green, purple and blue (not a blue rinse) added to our hair — usually by each other. There would be a heading of 'Crazy Colours' then a list of the particular combination being worn for the next few washes e.g. pink, blue, and green. A few pages later it would be: purple, orange, and red. We were out to make a statement! Maybe I will ask for bolder colour next time: copper, auburn, bright red? I could make a statement again, in my new chapter of life, 'maybs' as Sam says. Not sure I'm on for a Vivienne Westwood lookey likey but I'll give it some thought.

Thursday 30 May

I've done very little of interest these past two days — I've lacked energy, which I know is due to the illness, or the tablets, or both. Hoping it's a blip rather than a trend. Looking forward to tomorrow — the Centre — the highlight of my week.

Friday 31 May

Several hair compliments at the Centre! Lucas noticed it straight away. Said it was, 'happy hair' — no good for me then! A few of us sorted out a shopping list for tomorrow night and hit the cheap supermarket I'd never been to before. It was a whole new world — now I have earworm with the Disney song going round in my head...no! Instead of traipsing around in a permanent state of shock exclaiming, 'How much? I'm not paying that!' it was quite the reverse. Things were about forty percent cheaper than the bigger supermarkets (like a sad person, I worked it out). It was like going back a decade. I had never been because it's not my nearest one and I never had time to go further when I was working. I'll definitely start going now! Minika and Lucas were amused, anyway. They shop there all the time because it's near the hostel and are probably horrified at the cost of living in our country compared to their own. As a novice, I had to be educated in cheaper-supermarket-checkout-etiquette as the helpful young man showed me how to scoop everything into the trolley first, *then* sort it out 'over there' in order to keep the queue down and stop them from killing me for taking so long.

Food shopping is fun when it's not for the daily grind of existing. Twat was rubbish at it — so I did it, of course. Even when I was back in full time work, he engineered it so that it was terribly inconvenient for him and then would make sure he got the wrong brand or forgot things, in an attempt to prove that men were no good at shopping. We tried to keep Saturdays free to go places as a family or, later on, as a couple, but we never did. I always had schoolwork to do and after forcing him to help with the housework I had no energy left. As a consequence, I have hated food shopping ever since! I also now enjoy ready meals. It still feels like a guilty pleasure after all this time, but I had years and years of cooking. Needless to say, he was hopeless, or rather, lazy. So I did it all. And I helped Sam with homework, ran her around everywhere, all after a long day and a late finish due to the heavy burden of marking at least sixty books.

Q: Why didn't I say anything or make him do it, give him an ultimatum?

A: It was easier to do it myself than to have him huffing and puffing, effing and jeffing. I did it for a quiet life.

Naively, I assumed it would all change when I retired. Well it certainly did — but not in the way I'd anticipated. Remembering the time Sam came round one afternoon last year saying she'd been for a meal at Twat's house when *she* was out. Expecting Sam to complain about being served a baked bean sandwich or similar, she'd had frigging beef bloody stroganoff which *he* had cooked, exactly like mine! Bloody fraudulent pig. I knew he was a liar all along. And not purely about his finances. Anyway, that's all in the past now. How did I get carried away with that little rant? Oh yes, food shopping; it can be great fun.

June

Sunday 2 June

Writing this the day after — too late to write it last night!
A FANTASTIC NIGHT! On cloud nine and three quarters!
Best I've felt for months, if not years. Tons of money raised
for the Centre. Lucas insisted I dance with him, several
times. He's a great mover. We had such a laugh! He said I
was very 'rhythmic' and wants to go salsa dancing with me!
Thinking about it but it's probably against the volunteer
code, although it's not like we are starting a relationship; it
might count as helping him to enjoy himself? I used to go to
salsa classes with the girls from work, pre-stress days. I'm
hopeless at it. I have no coordination but can blag it, so I'm
told, and if you dance with someone who knows what
they're doing, they throw you around and make you look
vaguely proficient!

He's so nice. I bet he feels sorry for me as I told him I'm
divorced and live on my own. Simon kept whispering, 'He
fancies you,' like we were back at the youth club disco in
the seventies — before he was born! It was great craic. Told
him not to be ridiculous. The ceilidh dancing went down
well, although most people ended up being rebellious and
doing their own thing. Even the native English speakers in
the crowd found Joe, the caller with a lovely, broad Irish
accent, difficult to understand. Combined with the racket
made by clumsy people like me, jumping around, hopping
from foot to foot, spinning madly and dosey doe-ing, the
Centre clients didn't stand a chance! I knew how they felt:
exactly like I used to at the salsa classes! Joe, fed up with
cries of 'What?' from our little gang (the others being too
polite to do anything so rude) eventually gave up and the
band played jigs and reels galore whilst we free-styled the
rest of the night away. At that point, Lucas attempted to

show me some salsa steps to fit in with the music, a fascinating yet bizarre mix!

Minika was twirling and whirling Michael about like a rag doll! He would come over to us, periodically, pretending to be frightened, but judging by the cheeky grin on his face he was having a whale of a time. Ben joined in with gusto (ten more brownie points making a total of eleven). Even Hilary was up dancing with anyone and everyone, the rough red wine helping enormously to wash away any inhibitions! Simon came with his young barman called Nik, who is Greek. A serious but kind, gentle soul. 'The Gay Gordons' wasn't called after all. It must be out of vogue or, being a Scottish number, perhaps not included in an Irish ceilidh playlist — note the digital music storage reference — I'm getting there! Lucas made sure he asked everyone to dance, but I definitely danced with him the most. Listen to me... I sound like a fourteen-year-old! Sue and the other four women from school had great fun too. They reported that school hadn't changed at all, which I took to mean 'highly stressful'.

One of the young teachers, Hannah, was getting very friendly with Ahmed, a lovely young Syrian journalist, and they left together, in search of coffee at the late-night café. I'll have to email the others to get the low-down. I'm sure it would all be very innocent and as Hannah isn't a volunteer there's nothing to hide, unlike my potential misconduct at a salsa class!

Haven't felt this happy since Michael Gove was removed from his post as Education Secretary.

Monday 3 June

Received a flood of delightful texts and emails from nearly everyone who'd gone to the ceilidh telling me what a fab time they'd had and to let them know if there was anything similar in the future. Even Hilary was enthusing about it!

Think she secretly liked the attention from Lucas, even though she feigned disinterest and embarrassment when he or anyone else asked her to dance to the often unfathomable commands of old Joe. Firmly rooted in the 1950s, he insisted on telling the men to, 'Go get yerselves a pretty lady to dance with why don'tcha?' and, 'Now this is a one to get to know the ladies a lot better so it is!' in his tuneful Irish brogue. He wasn't aware that some of his audience were gay or lesbian and that ninety percent of the women were staunch feminists. Fortunately this all went over the heads of the Centre clients who understood very little but thoroughly enjoyed themselves. There was something beautiful about the fusion of African, Latin American, and Asian cultures putting their own slant on the Irish jigs. Each had their particular moves, originally created to be accompanied by different beats (not fiddle-de-dee) but somehow they melded into one delicious new rhythmic recipe. Like an episode of *Ready Steady Cook* but with an abundance of exotic ingredients — not the three mouldy ones from the back of the fridge — from a multitude of world cuisines, producing a prize-winning dish.

I have applied for my poetic licence for this one and will let you know when it arrives.

Tuesday 4 June

Lucas emailed me from the Centre! I seem to remember giving him my email address at some point in the evening. Must have been pre-wine or it would have been wrong! There is limited access to two computers there, always a queue and a timed waiting list to make it fair. Everyone wants news from home or to find out in their own language what is going on in their own country. The majority, of course, need it to check the progress of their case with the Home Office or their legal team who are spread very thinly across the region.

Anyway... he wants to know when we are going salsa dancing! Ever since my low point (when I looked like a wreck every day) Lucas has gone out of his way to ask how I am. He is a most intuitive man. I am VERY flattered and excited to the point of having butterflies in my stomach for the first time in what seems like a hundred years, but I am so nervous.

Against: This contravenes the Centre rules. Having a relationship with a client? You, madam, are henceforth barred from this establishment. It's no joking matter, I'd be devastated.

For: It's not a relationship, I'm simply helping a client to feel more in touch with his own culture and settle in, aren't I? Arguably, all part of the service. And, I'm certain he is just asking me so that he can meet other Latin American people (women) closer to his age who can dance properly! What's the harm in that?

No. It's wrong. It feels wrong. Argument over.

Wednesday 5 June

Emailed Lucas tonight with, 'Saturday.' Now super-nervous but can't mess him about and go back on my word. Decided against asking him if he wanted to eat somewhere first in case he thought I was trying to make it into some sort of date. I feel so sorry for him having no money and living on the breadline. Might be able to casually persuade him to eat at the Salsa Café where the dancing is. I can say I haven't eaten and don't want to eat alone.

I'll have to keep the whole thing quiet and hope no one from the Centre sees us in case people get the wrong idea. Shouldn't be stressing so much. After all, it's just another part of the voluntary work: salsa dancing with a younger, athletic, handsome, charismatic man. It's a dirty job but somebody's got to do it. Roll on Saturday!

Thursday 6 June

Sam called round on her way back from work. I made the fatal error of telling her about going to salsa on Saturday. Now she's wildly excited and acting as though it *is* a date. IT'S NOT! Tried telling her umpteen times that it was all part of my voluntary work, at which point she spat out her tea, laughing uproariously. Ignoring what I'd said, she started on the, 'What are you going to wear? You can't wear the same as you did at the ceilidh,' ad infinitum. Why not? I'm not a bloody celebrity. It's hardly likely that I'll be featured in next month's (or is it week's, never bought one in my life) *'Hi!'* magazine with, 'Lizzie Moffitt seen in same outfit twice in a row shocker...what's going on?' plastered across the front page.

I said, 'Sam, it's not a date,' in my teacher's voice, also wheeled out whenever she pushed the boundaries or overstepped the mark, usually as a teenager. That shut her up! Not telling the others as they will all react in exactly the same way. It's childish. Wonder if I can lose an inch off my waist in two days? There's a lot of waist-grabbing involved in salsa, unfortunately, especially if you need to be manoeuvred around the floor like I do. I'm wearing what I wore for the ceilidh — I think. Unless I decide to get something new.

Friday 7 June

Bad day. Went to the Centre hoping Lucas wouldn't call in, which he didn't, but was on tenterhooks all day in case he did! Forced myself to step over the threshold of the gym on the way back, with the intention of joining. I need to do some 'cardio vascular exercise' apparently, or so Simon says (sadly the rules of that game are you have to do whatever is required when 'Simon says'). Had the old tour I had twenty-two years ago after having Sam and deciding it was time to get the old bod into shape.

Even back then I thought it resembled a torture chamber more than a place that a supposedly sane person would choose in the name of 'leisure'; it hasn't changed. Although, the instruments of torture are now hi-tech and therefore much worse! Popped my head into one of the classes I used to go to. I recall the class being 'High Impact', during the heady era of aerobics, which contained a row of people Debs and I dubbed, 'the high impact wankers' — fitness-obsessed men and women who stood at the front and could grapevine for England. We would attempt to keep up, several rows back, giggling along to the music in an uncoordinated fashion.

'Combat', i.e. pretendy kicking and punching, looked to be more fun. Could get into that, but for the fact that they were all eighteen to twenty-five and I would be paranoid granny at the back. Showed me the hot tub (no thank you) and the sweaty steam rooms (yuk). Left with a price list, a non-committal, 'Thanks for your time,' and a still-oversized waistline. 'Can you pinch an inch?' the advert used to ask. 'No, but I can hang on to a bloody handful, will that do you?' Might look up liposuction. Haven't had alcohol since the ceilidh!

Saturday 8 June

Super Sensational Saturday!
Hell's bells I SNOGGED HIM! Or did *he* snog *me*? Can I ever face him again?
Don't know where to start — how about cloud ten! Hiked it up a notch; this one trumps the ceilidh. Decided not to ask him to go for anything to eat as I thought it unprofessional. UNPROFESSIONAL? You ain't seen nothin' yet (remember that song, oh ladies of Shady Pines, you lovely Shady Ladies?) *Unprofessional* tumbled onto the page, but

that's honestly what was in my head — at the time. So we met at the Salsa Café. A range of ages, with me in the minority as it wasn't OAP night, not that there is one. Nothing like I expected — Lucas chatted to a few South American people and some who were Spanish but he didn't dance with anyone except me! God he is so taut! Muscly, wiry, brown arms, six-to-eight-pack, stared into my eyes like a lovesick schoolboy and made me feel the same, except a girl version. Did a bit of 'holding close' which, as a teenager, would definitely have counted as 'getting off with' someone, but probably have its own separate list. It was all magical. 'Awesome,' Sara would say.

Had lots of chats between the dances. Told him about my life (unprofessional) THEN... yes the interesting bit that you've been waiting for and I want to prolong for ever because once I've written it I won't be keeping you in that delicious suspense any longer *and* the spell of it all might be broken. I'm sounding mad now. She's gone loopy again! Okay — then he walked me home and I was transported to the realms of fantasy, thinking of the line from the magnificent film *Brassed Off* when Tara Fitzgerald asks Ewan McGregor in for coffee and Ewan answers, 'I don't drink coffee,' then Tara says, 'I haven't got any.' Classic! The whole scene flashed through my unprofessional mind and I smiled to myself at having such an audacious thought. Managed to stop myself just in time and he would have answered either, 'No thank you, Lizzie,' or 'Yes please, Lizzie,' because he, unlike Ewan, does in fact drink coffee. Get to the point! Yes I am unashamedly savouring it, like eking out a good story, keeping the listeners hanging on for the punchline.

I said, 'Goodnight, Lucas. Thanks for a lovely nigh...,' and before I got the 't' out, he snogged me! Not a goodnight peck, you cynics, a fully-fledged, grown-up snog, the likes of which I thought I'd never experience again in my life — and probably won't. Cue the stars, bring on the chirping bluebirds! Then, realising I wouldn't see him for a whole week, drumroll for unprofessional act twenty-two of the evening, I blurted out, 'Do you want you come round for lunch on Monday?' adding, desperately, 'I promise not to use the microwave!' What an idiot! Holding my hand gently, he said, 'I would love to, Lizzie.' So I said, 'Great. One o'clock?' He gave me a goodnight peck and said, 'Perfecto!' Melt! After checking that we hadn't been followed by people who run the Centre or other potential spies, I picked myself up off the proverbial floor and went inside to still my beating heart with a glass of vino blanco and relive the whole thing through the magic of the diary! Whoo hoo!

Sunday 9 June

9.00 a.m. Oh Lord. What the hell have I done? I snogged a client. Well I could always plead that *he* did, in fact, snog *me*. Could say I was drunk, but that sounds even more irresponsible. He's got to be regretting it this morning, a consequence of salsa-induced madness, carried away in the Latino heat of the moment. 'Dios mío,' he will say to himself, 'I snogged that old volunteer woman.'

3.00 p.m. Checked email every half an hour — nothing to say he can't come tomorrow. Most likely explanation is that he can't get on a computer yet. Sunday is a busy day at the Centre. Not going food shopping until later or tomorrow when I know he'll have had a chance to use the computer and cancel. Although, he could be rude and cancel at the last minute — no, not his style. Oh God, what a fool I've made of myself and there's no fool like an old fool — the number of times I've said that! But it's always been in the context of a sixty plus rich man being taken to the cleaners by their twenty-five year old trophy wife who has divorced him after running off with her personal trainer, thus making: her a multi-millionaire; a small dent in his personal fortune;

a slightly larger dent in his pride, and leaving him wondering where he went wrong. Now *I* am that old fool, in all probability.

7.30p.m. I was bursting to offload onto someone so I chose Sara. The logic being: Sam would be too protective, Simon too over-the-top and excitable, and Hilary too shocked! Sara was delighted and unrealistically encouraging. I was hoping for some home truths and a stern reprimand — should have chosen Sam! Instead, Sara tried to convince me it was obvious that he was mad about me at the ceilidh — how he kept gravitating towards me all evening and coming back 'like a boomerang'. I pointed out that it's not a pleasant analogy as boomerangs were used to stun kangaroos and other prey in order to kill them, before returning to their original spot. I preferred not to think of Lucas as a boomerang. I fielded a barrage of questions from Sara which took me back to my high school days:

Did you do tongues?

Was it 'gorge' or sloppy?

He didn't hold your face in his hands, did he?

Answers:

A bit.

'Gorge'.

Don't be ridiculous.

We giggled a lot — exactly like teenagers. It was superb fun! She was adamant he would turn up as arranged, claiming smugly that she knows about these things. Hmm, maybe he will, maybe he won't. And it definitely won't be at the designated time of one o'clock because in Colombia all social arrangements are entirely approximate and subject to delay, he tells me! When I told her that, I found myself adding, 'He's not that rude though,' to which she quipped, 'See, you're defending him already! You like him, you trust him and you know he'll turn up, possibly even on time. Sussed!' I swore her to secrecy and she left me feeling gloriously giddy.

Ventured to the shops in search of chicken and veg, a lemon torte and wine — is that sensible? You know what happened last time. Yes I need it to calm my shredded nerves. Can't exactly start on the vodka at one thirty in the afternoon, he'll think (know) I've got a problem.

Monday 10 June

Mad, moreish Monday.
Need to write the rest tomorrow... mmmmm... cloud eleven.

Tuesday 11 June

12.00 noon. Yesterday is a day I will remember and cherish for the rest of my life, even if it proves to be the day before I was sacked from my job as a volunteer. Can you be sacked from an unpaid job — barred, dropped, banned, defrocked? I am about to find out! Unprofessional conduct four: invited client to lunch. Canoodled, which also incorporated snogging, on volunteer's sofa until something like 'midnight o'clock' as Lucas calls it, cutely. Guilty as charged. Shouldn't joke about it.

Flapped around with food all morning making sure everything was ready as I knew the nerves would never stand up to chit-chat while cooking. I'd be bound to drop, burn, forget, and ruin everything in the process. When Lucas arrived he was relaxed and as lovely as ever. He'd brought me flowers. I was embarrassed because the amount of money a refugee can claim is incredibly small. Without the Centre providing occasional meals for them, some wouldn't eat for days. Greeted me with a peck on both cheeks, as they do in most warm-blooded countries, but that's everyone, not restricted to the middle classes and luvvies like it is here! Food went down well, from what I can remember. Talked more about our past lives. He'd had a long term partner, Natalia, for ten years until he was thirty-two. Also a teacher, they split up when he became active in the union. She was frightened, and he feared for her safety as he knew that the threats would be extended to the partners and families of those targeted. The relationship became too fraught so he had to choose between his partner and his politics. Knowing he would be in a better position than most to speak out with no ties, no dependants, he told her he couldn't stand by in silence or he would be racked with guilt for the rest of his life. Of course it was heartbreaking for them, but at least she would be safe and not subject to death threats. Natalia understood his choice very well, being of the same political leaning, but how tragic for both of them! I was moved to tears when he told me, as was he.

I divulged more about Twat, how he'd shattered my dreams and how I felt after retiring. Told him everything, actually! Talked about becoming older, feeling invisible, demoted to a lower position in society's eyes through my age and status: retired, single. He could identify with that in terms of coming to Britain as an asylum seeker. 'Before, a teacher, now a beggar,' he said. Begging for shelter, for food, for invisibility from his pursuers and for a new life, for which he would be so grateful. But he also feels the invisibility of his new status as a refugee: demoted — with many people assuming he has come to 'scrounge benefits', possessing an innate knowledge of how to 'work the system', the tabloids tell us with great authority. I felt desperately sad for him at times but he always saved the moment by adding a touch of humour to it. Sara would say there was absolutely no need to draw attention to my age and I could get away with forty on a good day, but this was an open, honest exchange and I felt totally comfortable and at ease. All the while he was saying the right (if untrue) things; when I complained about my ageing body and my facial lines he said the words, 'But you are beautiful,

Lizzie,' as he held my hand, pulled me towards him and kissed me gently, over and over.

Simon might have said something like, 'Sounds like the AGM of the Mutual Appreciation Society.' Well here are the minutes, my lovely friends, recorded for posterity and because I can't quite believe that it really happened — to me! So... *that's* how it went all evening, snuggled up on the sofa, egged on silently by the wine — or rather, *I* was. He didn't drink much, again showing up the British and their alcohol-orientated reputation! I spent hours running my hand over his toned chest and arms — all incredibly beautiful. We indulged in 'arm stroking', which would also have counted as getting off with someone as a teenager. At midnight o'clock he said he ought to be going. How I stopped myself from asking him to stay, I will never know. But I did, and feel good about it now (not at the time) thus swerving professional misconduct number five.

Wednesday 12 June

10.30 p.m. Early night required. I'm enjoying churning over the events of Monday in my head, although the churning stomach is guilt-related as well as due to excitement. Texted Sara telling her that it was 'lovely'. I want to savour this myself for as long as possible. Oh God, what if he's a spy, a murderer or a fraudster? He might be a drug dealer (now I'm being racist) trying to gain the confidence of a vulnerable older, stupid, and easily flattered woman? Maybe he was secretly eyeing up the sensible storage systems in the kitchen or checking out the bath panel to see if it comes apart easily for drug-stashing purposes. After all, why would he be genuinely interested in spending time with a moaning old wine-swigging thing like me? This can't happen again.

No word from him today. Probably having massive regrets. Either that or he's been on his secret phone all day to the cartel.

Friday 14 June

After the hideous online dating and email-checking fiasco, I am trying to remain composed and dignified by limiting myself to three checks per day. Nothing today (or yesterday, but that's too depressing to report). Helped Ahmed at the Centre to find suitable clothes from the donations room. He was very grateful. I was dying to ask about Hannah, but Sam's 'embarrassed daughter' face popped into my head so I didn't dare! Spent a restless evening faffing around until I allowed myself to open some wine as it's Friday. Feeling much better — I think it's what you'd call 'alcoholism'?

Saturday 15 June

In an effort to remain calm, I went for a walk to take my mind off the situation and discovered that the Hoppings has arrived! It takes over a week to set up as it's the biggest travelling fair in Europe and undoubtedly one of the highlights of every Newcastle child's year. From as far back as I can remember, the top four events in my life were:

1) Birthday.
2) Christmas.
3) Easter.
4) Hoppings.

All of the above involved treats or presents and huge amounts of fun. I can recall the pangs of abject misery when, after a week on the Town Moor spent entertaining kids and adults alike, the Hoppings packed up and rolled away into the late, summer sunset for another whole long year. I would console myself with the comforting thought that my birthday was only five months away, giving me a reason to live and cheering up my face, much to the relief of my parents. I had the same feeling when the Christmas tree and decorations were taken down on or before the sixth of January — back to mundane reality and school.

The Hoppings is sensory heaven: the smell of candy floss, chips, and freshly cut grass hits you immediately. A heady and unique mixture transports you back to your childhood, as though nothing in the world has ever changed, sending endorphins racing around your body with the message, 'We're about to have some serious fun, here!' The music, always the latest popular tunes, blares out from flashing, spinning images — Waltzer, Hurricane, Tagada — each one shining brighter as night draws in. The rules are:

1) Eat candy floss — a taste exclusive to a fairground.

2) Try to win, and if not, buy a coconut that will later be ceremoniously smashed with a hammer by your dad, having been drilled first to release the coconut milk only ever consumed after the Hoppings. No one had ever heard of Thai curry.

As a teenager, it was an event involving weeks of forward planning i.e. what to wear for the Hoppings. One year I went in my favourite Bay City Rollers outfit. Mine was 'Eric' tartan. Not sure which clan that particular design originated from — oh yes… the BCR clan of course! Gran did a great job of sewing strips of it up the sides of the baggy jeans and you always bought enough to make a scarf to tie around your wrist. Bainbridge's department store did a roaring trade in tartan that year — happy days! I must tell Lucas about my tartan trendiness! What I probably won't tell him is that once I snogged a swarthy traveller boy who reminded me of David Essex in *That'll be the Day*. I had an early taste of rejection when I returned the next night to hang around the Waltzer, and was completely ignored; ditched for a much prettier and older girl! Yes, we have always been either too young or too old.

It was also my first encounter with different cultures, apart from two lovely girls in my class from Indian families, both of whom I adored. I was enthralled with their deliciously different food and the beautiful furnishings, paintings and ornaments that adorned their houses. The Hoppings offered a glimpse into the travelling culture too. I loved walking past the ornate, immaculate caravans and taking a sneaky peek inside. Needless to say, I would gladly have run away with any one of them who asked or kidnapped me as I was convinced it would be the best life ever, living on candy floss and coconuts, having free rides every day, all year round — heaven! Ah, the naivety of youth.

Who you were going to the Hoppings with was also the subject of great debate and excitement. If a boy you fancied was in your designated Hoppings crowd, you might be able to squash on a ride with him, or pretend to be terrified and cling on to him — very girlie but worth a try. There was no such thing as being too scared to experience any of the torturous, stomach-churning, vertigo-inducing rides. Looking at them now, I can't imagine how I managed to survive them, yet I genuinely wasn't frightened — I was in my element! Strange, how age induces an increasing awareness of perceived danger and the drastic measures your body will go to in order to protect you from it. It was after a whirl on the Big Wheel as a thirtysomething that I developed a fear of heights I'd never experienced before. I distinctly remember thinking, 'Errrr …I don't like this!' as I swung around precariously, suspended in mid-air. As a result I had a fully blown panic attack on the London Eye two years later. Hideously embarrassing as my fellow captive passengers in the glass pod shuffled uncomfortably from foot to foot, some asking if I was okay, but every last one of them wondering if or when this mother was going to blow and what would be the outcome given that we were one hundred and thirty-five metres above the ground (I looked it up later) moving at the pace of a snail with the prospect of escape at least twenty-five minutes away! Would she stop doing that funny breathing and start hurling herself at the glass, demanding to be let out, or turn hysterical, further upsetting the children and ruining it for all who'd paid the twenty-plus pounds for the pleasure? Still, the Youtube footage might have compensated for the annoyance at the time, had I obliged. Luckily (or boringly) for them, I stuck it out, eyes squeezed shut, clinging to the seat with one hand and to my friend, fortunately not short-tempered Twat, with the other, trying to control my breathing. Excluding childbirth, it was the longest twenty-five minutes of my life and biggest waste of twenty-plus quid ever. At least the Big Wheel was a mere one pound fifty at the time.

A trip from the Centre to the Hoppings was being discussed when I was there on Friday. Won't be able to go on any rides but might stretch to candy floss for all from our ceilidh proceeds and simply enjoy the atmosphere, with the added bonus of temporarily diverting attention from life's troubles for all participants. I do hope Lucas goes. Already feeling like a teenager again!

Tuesday 18 June

FINALLY — an email! After the third check it arrived, luckily, or I wouldn't have been able to pick it up until tomorrow! It said how sorry he was for not having thanked me for a wonderful evening, but he'd been to the Centre a few times recently to use the computers and the queue had been too long. He'd also gone to the Centre on Friday to see me but I'd left five minutes before he arrived. And yes, I do believe him, before anyone casts aspersions upon his character! Asked if I would be going to the Hoppings on Friday. I replied straight away because I'm too old to play games and I trust this man. Don't ask me why, I just do.

Thursday 20 June

Can't wait for the Hoppings tomorrow! I bet there's a diary lurking somewhere in that box with exactly the same entry as this if I look hard enough. As I said earlier, I feel like a teenager again!

Friday 21 June

Hoppings trip surpassed all expectations! We raised enough money from the ceilidh to buy everyone candy floss, ice cream or a toffee apple. Simply walking around, soaking up the atmosphere was enough of a treat and it proved a brief respite from thinking about asylum claims, recent traumas and worrying about loved ones back home.

For me, it was like being back at high school, with Lucas there after our shenanigans from last Monday night! My heart was thumping in time to the music being blasted out from the rides and I had to breathe deeply in an effort to control it. I kept catching him looking at me, smiling, and was convinced that Ken or the other volunteers would be able to see right through our veneer of normality. Nothing to see here, move along to the dodgems everyone. It was a mixture of excruciating and exciting — a reflection of our surroundings with people screaming with terror one minute and shrieking with laughter, the next. We went to the amusement arcade to see what used to be called the 'Penny Falls' — where you drop in a penny and the logs move across, hopefully pushing a small fortune of at least eight pennies your way. Success! Though, due to twenty-first century inflation, they now cost either two pence or ten pence! Undeterred, some of the gang sampled the joys of the 'Two-penny Falls' — all good fun.

The Ghost Train was hilarious to watch and I was glad to see that there are still people working there, dressed as skeletons, whose job it is to jump out and frighten the living daylights out of the innocent passengers in their carriages as they pass through. It gave me a chance to tell my ghost train story, or at least the censored version without the profanities of the original:

When we were in our teens, Debs threatened the poor Ghost Train skeleton, who was simply doing his job, snarling (season with own swear words as required), 'If you so much as come anywhere near me I'm going to punch your lights out, sunshine!' I couldn't quite believe it. Her defence was that she was so terrified he was going to ruffle her perfectly coiffed her, that the words came out involuntarily! Needless to say, we laughed till we couldn't breathe. Lucas particularly enjoyed the story and everyone learned a new idiom in the form of 'to punch one's lights out'.

It was an unforgettable evening; one I shall treasure for ever. Luckily, it is safely documented here in the diary, should my memory fail me in old age.

Tuesday 25 June

Did very little today, apart from luxuriate in the warm glow still surrounding me from Friday — and the previous Monday! Trying not to let it take over my life, as that's unhealthy for the fragile body and soul that I'm doing my damnedest to keep together.

Saw Sam on Sunday. She and Ben are ecstatically happy and I have to accept that I won't be seeing as much of her as I did when she was between boyfriends. It was ever thus.

Friday 28 June

A very productive day at the Centre! Didn't see Lucas but managed to help a newly-arrived Nigerian man to get in contact with other refugees from his country for support and help with his claim. He was extremely thin and looked exhausted, but left the Centre smiling and chatting to one of the group who had come to help him. Days such as these make everyone feel good about themselves.

I don't think anyone realises how much I cherish being a part of that place. I mustn't jeopardise it.

July

Monday 1 July

LUCAS EMAILED! He asked if I'd like to go down to the Laing Art Gallery (free entry) on Thursday — what's wrong with tomorrow? Haven't been there for years. You become blasé when it's on your own doorstep. There are so many things to do and see in this city yet I am so useless that it takes someone from another country to arrange it. He told me how much he'd enjoyed the other Monday — that's all, one sentence — enough for me. Said I'd meet him at midday o'clock. I could buy him lunch then. Oh no, he might think I'm trying to swap food for compliments or sex. There, I said it — it just fell out of the pen again, it wasn't me. GET A GRIP OF YOUR PEN, MOFFITT! Had to go for a brisk walk to stop myself going mad. Called Sam and told her I'd had a quiet week which, on paper, is true! However, she said she could sense a change in my mood. Am I that transparent? I do *not* want my whole life and happiness to revolve around a man again! Look what happened last time: it swallowed up nearly a quarter of a century of my life. No, I shall remain in control — do I hear derisory laughter emanating from the Shady Pines gang who know the ending of this story when I don't? I sincerely hope not.

Simon emailed demanding to know why I was giving him the silent treatment. Arranged to see him on Wednesday. Suddenly I'm in demand and have an air of mystery about me. Haven't achieved that since I had my upper lip burnt having it waxed at a dubious beauty salon and had to stay indoors for a week, refusing all offers of socialising.

Sue also emailed with the excellent news that Hannah and Ahmed are going to meet up next weekend for a fundraising picnic at Hannah's church. How sweet! I feel like cupid, although some of my arrows have travelled to places that are strictly forbidden. Must ask Ahmed more about his life and how he ended up here. Other than the fact he is a journalist from Syria, I know nothing about him. Most people are happy to tell you their life story; talking can be therapeutic. For others, however, it is all very raw and they are much too traumatized to verbalise it yet.

Tuesday 2 July

Sam called me. I swear she has a gossip radar, or maybe it's because she's becoming suspicious. She told me she knew immediately I was hiding something yesterday so I was cajoled into telling her about Lucas coming round the other week and that we were getting 'quite close', which was a mistake because she jumped to the conclusion that it must be a fully blown relationship and started asking if I thought I was ready for one and all the rest of it; it seemed to go on for ages. I lied to my own daughter because I had to play the whole thing down, claiming it was mainly platonic, in an attempt to shut her up. I may well regret it if things continue as they are, or escalate, because I will have to have this conversation all over again! Flaming heck, once is bad enough!

Wednesday 3 July

Met Simon on his day off. His job's so interesting: a designer for a publishing company, mainly book covers. 'You can, and should, judge a book by its cover,' is his motto! It accommodates his creative brain and quirky sense of humour. Felt compelled to tell him about Le Weekend as I think of it. Omitted a few details as I felt too disloyal (to both Lucas and Sam) to dissect the evening as I would once have done and report every move made by him or me.

'No we didn't, Simon,' 'Yes it was, Simon,' 'Yes we did a bit,' 'Yes he was, Simon,' 'No it certainly was not!' was how the conversation went, with him attempting, cunningly through years of practice, to fill in the gaps with detailed, closed questions. So, I suppose he knew practically everything by the time he'd reached the bottom of the second glass of skinny latte. 'He wheedled it out of me, Your Honour. I didn't tell him a thing!'

'Well you're a dead ringer for a woman in lurve,' Simon taunted, before launching into the rest of the Meatloaf track while I squirmed with embarrassment and everyone in the packed café stared over at the whole spectacle! When I could finally get a word in, I told him not to be so ridiculous and how I'd never heard anything so stupid and not to be so disrespectful to his elders and any other defensive retort I could think of. The combined voices of 10CC sang 'I'm Not in Love' in my head all the way home. They're a bloody annoying bunch once they start. Had flipping earworm all night with it, thanks to that lot!

I'll have to tell Sam at some point soon. It's not fair on her to be lower than position three on the list of people who know the truth about the Lucas situation.

Thursday 4 July at last!

Had one of those unforgettable days from *Airplane II,* when Leslie Nielsen and Priscilla Presley go to the baseball game, funfair, and beach, all to the tune of 'I'm Into Something Good' by Herman's Hermits. Haven't had a day like it since before meeting Twat because, well … he was too boring I suppose, and we were friends for a long time before getting together so there was never that *Airplane II* moment. We knew each other too well. Anyway, enough of him. Went to the gallery and discussed the paintings in a half-intellectual, half-silly way. Lucas knows a lot about art. He knows a lot about everything, actually.

I suggested lunch in the park. Decided to bring a picnic as I didn't want to keep emphasising the fact that he has no money, so he was delighted when I produced sandwiches, biscuits and juice (containing no alcohol for appearances' sake). It earned me a massive hug and a kiss! Yes, I'd snog someone who surprised me with food from their bag, too. In fact, I'd snog *anyone* who surprised me with food from their bag. I adore his English accent but to hear him speak Spanish is like drinking melted chocolate, poured from a jug (mixing my sensory similes here but my poetic licence is nearly through, so they tell me).

All day I felt like it wasn't really happening to me. It was as if I were watching myself in a film — too good to be true. Glimpsed at my reflection in a window on the way to the bus stop and was shocked — there was a smiling, relaxed, happy looking person. No lines were visible (due to insufficient light) on that face. I must hold onto that image when I'm feeling down again. Perhaps I should allow people to talk to me only when I'm standing in front of a window at dusk. Alas, the euphoria was short-lived. I had to spoil it by worrying in case anyone had seen us for the entire journey home. I know it's not against the law, but it is against the rules of the Centre and is, at the very least, disrespectful. Selfishly, I don't want tongues wagging and people secretly laughing at the old fool, or tut-tutting at what could be regarded as an exploitative relationship. *There*, I said 'relationship'. We are NOT having a relationship!

I grew more and more paranoid then said that I had to go and meet Sam (a lie). So, after some sensible goodbye pecking, I scurried home to martyrdom, weeding the garden as a punishment for being such a bad person. HELP! I don't know *what* to think!

Friday 5 July

Words of wisdom from Simon and an email from Lucas!
Simon — told me to: give myself a break, stop beating myself up, and asked if I was ever satisfied. Also said it was: nobody's business, we were grown-ups and just because I can't believe my luck doesn't mean I don't deserve it or shouldn't enjoy it! End of sermon.
Lucas — thanked me for the day out, said how much he'd enjoyed it and asked when he could next see me! After Simon's pep talk I felt I was allowed to reply, 'How about tomorrow night?' Oh well, in for a penny.

I went underwear shopping after my shift at the Centre.
Underwear Shopping
Simon would have given his right arm to come with me but I forbade it. I ignored his pleas and kind offers of help i.e. 'I can advise you, Lord knows you'll need it after so long!' Thanks!

Managed it myself, by a whisker. Went up-market and out of my comfort-bra zone so wouldn't be surrounded by teenagers and twentysomethings buying cute lacy items that look like they were made for mice. As I entered the changing room I also refused the offer of help from the women in the shop. I wanted to ask, 'What sort of help do you have in mind? Do you think I look like I'll need assistance with hoisting them up from around my waist and bundling them kicking and screaming into their straightjacket? I'm not that old you know!' However, I replied, 'No thank you.'

Ignored Simon's parting words of, 'It's got to be black or red,' and bought some lovely sets in various colours (not white but not black or red either). Not a smidgeon of lace in sight — literally no frills — except not very cheap. Wow, the elastic straps are properly elasticated and don't drop over your shoulders even on the tightest setting, AND none of the fasteners are broken! Yet another whole new world: a new world of underwear. A whole new underworld.

Saturday 6 July

12.00 noon o'clock. Can't WAIT for tonight! Might have to do some more weeding to take my mind off it, that's how utterly and completely obsessed I am.

Sunday 7 July

Whoop, whoop whoop! May the good Lord (if he exists) strike me down... if so he won't have far to travel because I'm up here on cloud eleven! Are you Shady Ladies ready for this? After twenty-four years of sleeping with the same person, and at least three years since I even did that, I slept with another man! Yes, Lucas of course, I'm not that quick a worker and yes, it was brilliant! Have patience, and I will divulge a few details.

He insisted on cooking for us so I bought the ingredients for that delicious chicken dish he'd made at the Centre. Yes, I will get to the juicy bit soon. Really, ladies ... at *your* age! Like all good Latin American romantic novels, food and sex go hand in hand. The signs were there when he did what we used to call, 'pre-sex war dance', do you recall, ladies? Whereby sexually attracted couples engage in silly play-fighting, slapping, chasing and such like. It's an excuse to get close to each other and have physical contact, similar to the birds and creatures the world over who engage in courtship rituals.

Lots of tickling, nudging out of the way, and feigned annoyance took place during the food preparation; always a good sign. We ate quickly and returned to the sofa where we were soon entwined, kissing. Savouring every moment, I swam in his absolute loveliness, drinking it in, gulping it down, like drowning in chocolate — what a way to go.

Didn't give a thought to the no-gym-membership body, nor to the waistline or the ever-present stomach fat. There was no need; he made me feel like I was twenty-five, not fifty-five. It came as a huge surprise, no pun intended, that sex could be so oh-oh-oh good! It was reminiscent of my twenties, pre-Twat days, but I had a defence mechanism at the ready: I erased good sex from my memory after him, lest I became discontented with my lot and went in search of it, which I would have done, had I remembered it like this.

Yes, we did it again in the morning, after I'd brushed and flossed my teeth, sorted out my bird's nest hair and removed last night's smudged mascara. Generous and forthcoming with his compliments though he was, there are limits to everyone's ability to see that beauty is only skin deep and I, for one, wasn't going to risk pushing my luck.

Strangely enough, I don't feel as panicky as before, when I had merely snogged him. It feels right (although technically, the Refugee Centre rulebook states categorically that it isn't) and it feels comfortable. But comfortable is what I must definitely not allow myself to become. This gorgeous man may have found his way into my life at the exact moment I most needed him, but he is merely passing through it. He is not mine and he is not here to stay. I will take a photo of him for my memory box, or for the diary. You might be looking at it now! I hope you are, then you will be sure to remember him and the happiness he bestowed on me, all those years ago.

Monday 8 July

Spent the entire day basking, not just in sunshine, but in the memories of Saturday night: smooth brown skin, stretched taut over muscular limbs, a voice like honey, soothing and warm. Is this sounding rom-com-esque? I'm afraid I can't help myself! He makes me want to wax lyrical, to sing, to whistle (sod the lip-lines). I feel *alive* again — normal. I'm not properly normal as in: how I should feel most of the time. No, I am hyper-obsessive, manic as in: too-much-caffeine manic. It's anything but normal, it's utterly FANTASTIC!

Tuesday 9 July

Met Sara for lunch and blabbed. I had to. She's now more excited than I am! 'Ah, man it's lush!' she kept saying, and, 'You little devil!' with the Geordie twang making it sound even more wicked!

Called Sam to update her. Decided not to admit to being economical with the truth during our last discussion, but was compelled to confess that things were no longer platonic. More hyper-enthusiasm, with — Sam being Sam — a note of caution attached, 'You're not getting too involved are you, Mum?' The voice of reason, my conscience, the part I am trying to ignore but know I have to address soon. 'I'm onto it, don't worry.' I know all too well how this will pan out, but I do want to take the lid off this delicious box of chocolates again, sample more of its delights and maybe even delve into the next layer before putting it back on the shelf, out of reach. After all, I will remind you again ladies, that the new underwear wasn't cheap.

Thursday 11 July

10.00 a.m. My heart is engaged in hand-to hand combat with my head. My heart is winning. I am trying to remain cool, calm and collected — fat chance! Make a list.

Head	Heart
This is wrong on a number of levels:	This feels so right:
• Professional misconduct (though it isn't my profession).	• Good for my physical and mental wellbeing, if not his.
• He will move away one day.	• Makes me deliriously happy.
• I'm too old.	• Makes me feel young, attractive, interesting, and valued.
• He will probably look for a younger woman eventually.	• I'm having high quality sex.
• I don't want to get saddled with another bloke — I want to live life on my terms for a change.	• We are so compatible.
	• I love seeing him.

I declare the heart, in the red corner, a WINNER! Not the result I wanted, but it was out of my hands, Your Honour.
Head: I shall be the judge of that.
Heart: Shut up, you.
3.00 p.m. He emailed! Wants to walk along the river this evening.
Heart: Can I have a teeny bit more please, I have her under control. It was always the plan to see him for a little longer then calm it down.
Head *(in a Chicago accent)*: Who d'ya think you're kiddin' lady? I wasn't born yesterday.

Heart: No need to rub it in, Head, I'm well aware of how old I am. I'm sure I can handle it. How about a weency little bit more, please?

Head *(still in a Chicago accent)*: Shuddup why don'tcha? You obviously made up ya mind already. Do whatcha want, lady. See if I care.

Heart: Okay, I will.

So that's settled, then. I'll tell him to meet me at the Millennium Bridge at seven. Zip it, Head!

Saturday 13 July

10.00 p.m. A very early night is called for!

Yes ladies, you are now likely to be *very* interested in this part of the diary. Has it jogged your memories? If Debs and Chris are there with you as you read it, as it was always meant to be — the three of us in Shady Pines, reunited in our old age, inseparable in our youth — do you all remember me telling you about the evening in question?

Met at the beautiful Millennium Bridge. Walked and talked right up to the Free Trade Pub. Had a quick drink then ambled back again. Shattered but needed to burn off the pent-up nervous energy. It was pure bliss. Came back here and ate cheese on toast (he loves English cheese!) then listened to salsa music I had downloaded — yes, me! Very proud of myself! Acted as if I did it all the time. His legal team are confident he has a good case for Leave to Remain. Need to mentally prepare myself for:

Deportation — surely not?

Dispersal — sent to another part of the country once Leave to Remain is granted — possible.

Head *(still adopting that ludicrous accent)*: You'd betta brace ya'self, lady.

I am prolonging the lush bit, keeping you in suspense — ladies of the care home. You will not be disappointed, I assure you. Enjoyed a wee bit of salsa dancing in the lounge, not for long as I was too tired but couldn't admit to it in case it made me sound old and past-it. Good excuse to get close. Hadn't held hands on the walk — was in professional mode. One funny — he said I was a very 'sensible' woman, which I first thought was a crap thing to say, not a compliment at all, before realising that 'sensible' means 'sensitive' in Spanish, not boring! We had a good laugh about it. As he said, 'Who wants to be sensible?'

Bed: W.O.W. — that means wow and is not an acronym. Hang on a minute, could be 'Wild Or What?' It was simply gorgeous. I must *not* get used to this. Anyhow, the best thing he said was, 'How could anyone leave you, lovely Lizzie?' I could have cried. Then he sang — in Spanish of course — very sexy. Melted again, like chocolate, melted chocolate. Messy and luscious. He said I didn't snore. Not so sure about that.

He left after scrambled eggs on toast. No jokes please, ladies, about scrambling my eggs because that corner of the cupboard is almost certainly bare! Yuk — sorry.

Sunday 14 July

Sam called; she sounded worried about me. She's going all maternal and role-reversal-ish on me: 'Don't get too involved (again) he might get deported.' Let's all look on the bright side shall we? Told her that would be a tragedy but not for me. I am in control and fine. She thinks I'm vulnerable because I am on antidepressants. I told her I was going to ask about coming off them — yes I *did* think it was a good idea and no I *wouldn't* do it myself and does she think I'm that stupid etcetera, etcetera. Get the picture? Maybe I'll hang on before making the appointment — not telling Sam though. Tricky business, this 'daughter knows best' thing. It certainly takes some getting used to.

An evening surprise landed in my inbox (again not a euphemism) from Lucas. It was sent at five o'clock from the Centre. He said I could read it again before going to bed then it would make sense! Thanked me for yesterday, 'for the evening, the night and the morning' and for looking after him so well throughout this 'difficult and crazy time'. He is so thoughtful and generous. I am not the one who is vulnerable. There's a reason why it's against the rules.

Wednesday 17 July

Incident on the Metro

Saw a young, well-dressed, ordinary looking bloke grope a woman's bottom as she got off the Metro. She turned around on the platform, shouting at him to eff off, then the doors closed and that was the end of it, or so he thought. Spurred on by Sam challenging the builders a few months ago and a recent injection of self-confidence, I took over the shouting and yelled, 'Yes, I saw what you did! Don't you DARE touch a woman like that. It's disgusting!' I felt the anger welling up, engulfing my throat, constricting my voice, forcing it to become lower and lower — akin to a growl, with every word. I was pointing at him, keeping my distance in case he lunged at me. He attempted to say, 'It was a joke, man,' until he was silenced with, 'Shut up!'

Sara said later that I was 'brilliant but barmy' as he might have had a knife, 'or been a real radge-pot' as she put it. I didn't care at the time, I couldn't have simply stood by, having witnessed it, without giving him a piece of my mind. It may be a slightly unhinged mind, and I wouldn't wish even a small piece of it on most people, but a groper deserves a generous helping of it for what he did — and he got it.

Luckily for me it had the desired effect and he wasn't armed, dangerous or even abusive. I think he was shocked at the level of ranting and attempted to laugh it off until he was told, in no uncertain terms, 'It's no laughing matter, that's sexual assault!' A voice from the back of the carriage confirmed, 'Yes it is!' Stunned into silence, he assumed the stance of a reprimanded child, muttering, 'Aalreet, aalreet man,' in a way that suggested the message had indeed filtered through. Satisfied my mission was complete, I stomped off and sat down with my back to everyone and my heart thumping, hoping that the public shaming wouldn't backfire and end up with me being his next target. To my great relief, he got off at the next station.

Note of caution: this type of public-spirited action is not good for blood pressure! The second I got home I rang Sam then Sara and recounted the whole tale. I was reassured that, on balance, I had done the right thing. I wanted to tell Lucas but will save it for another time, in case it sends him running for the hills.

Friday 19 July

Centre was lovely. The great news is that Michael has secured ILR status: *Indefinite* Leave to Remain. It's the golden ticket for any refugee as it offers peace of mind and security at last. Freedom from fear of the authorities arriving in the night to deport you to the country you fled. For many, it means they are saved from certain death. Freedom to work and contribute properly to society, which means so much to Michael. 'I am not a lazy man,' he would say repeatedly, frustrated at a law dictating that he could not work until ILR was granted.

He will be a huge miss — always eager to lend a hand with any jobs that needed doing in the Centre. I mustn't worry about him. He will find a job easily because he's skilled and willing to have a go at anything; a reliable, dependable, diligent soul. We had the customary mini-party. When someone secures ILR, juice and cake are handed around by the successful client. It is a joyful ritual of the place. 'Lizzie, I thank you very much for your help,' Michael said. Another humbling moment. All I do is turn up once a week, make a few sandwiches and chat to people. It's hardly worthy of special thanks. I don't even know his story, other than he was a farmer and is a Christian. I will find the right moment to ask him sometime. Lucas came in at the end. I noticed how much he contributes to the atmosphere of a room as he congratulated and joked with Michael. When he flashed me a smile, I had butterflies more fluttery than any you might find in the rainforest, and they're pretty damn fluttery, so I'm told.

Sunday 21 July

Newcastle Pride (Saturday)
I have always been immensely proud of my city and never more so when annual events like Pride come around, hugely supported by the entire community — a family day of fun. A chance for LGBTQIA people to feel relaxed about public displays of affection without fear of offending a bigot or, on occasions, being verbally or physically assaulted. Ironically, Lucas and I weren't able to indulge in PDA as ours is now the clandestine relationship, though for how much longer it will be either clandestine or a relationship is anyone's guess.

I met him there, growing more and more nervous as the time approached when he was due to arrive. When I saw him, my stomach leapt into my throat and I turned beetroot red — God, I'm so transparent! Almost shouted, 'Hi!' in a very high-pitched 'fancy seeing you here' squeak, in case anyone was spying on us. Pathetic really, like having an affair — which I suppose we are doing. Never arrive at or leave a place together or people will suspect. Otherwise they will never ever know. Not that I've had one — it's just what I've heard. Acting as if we weren't seeing each other nor having some sort of clandestine relationship was strangely exhilarating. Not sure of its proper title. This must be how it feels to have a real affair. I can appreciate that the teenage, jittery excitement, the adrenalin rush, and nervousness are what motivates people to continue the risk of being discovered. Feelings evocative of youth — exquisite!

Lucas was impressed by the sheer numbers there, showing support for the event. They have Pride Weekend in Bogota, and the situation is slowly improving, but there remains a substantial degree of discrimination against the gay community at both state and social level, he told me. Years ago, gay people had to take extra care at night as there were armed gangs who would target them as they left a club, leaving their bodies on the street as a warning to others.

Difficult to imagine such atrocities, yet, some of you may remember that homosexuality was illegal in England and Wales until 1967 and remained so in Scotland and Northern Ireland until 1980 and 1982! I know this because Lucas asked me, so I looked it up. In Colombia it was also 1981 — second out of the last three! It's shocking to think that throughout my secondary school years it was illegal to be gay in nearby Scotland. I had gay friends at school, but not many who had come out by then. Hardly surprising when, less than two hours up the road, it was a criminal offence.

Pride has a funfair with a handful of rides; it's no Hoppings! There are stalls galore selling anything and everything rainbow, food stalls, and clothing. Every trade union and community group for miles around is represented. The fact that unions are promoting themselves in a public place, not confined strictly to the realms of the workplace, was a culture shock in itself for Lucas. When I was working, I used to volunteer for a shift on the National Education Union stall so Lucas and I dropped by to see the people I know. Every year they become fewer, no they haven't died, they've retired and been replaced by the younger generation, which is great for the union. He enjoyed talking to the members on the stall about the differences between the two countries and the state's attitude towards unions. They were fascinated and I felt so proud to know him, to be with him.

The bands were great, as was the MC — a drag artist called Camilla who was very funny without being outrageous, given the family audience! Lucas laughed along but I know he struggled to understand most of it. We encountered the festival's obligatory drunken teenager. A young girl, clearly the worse for wear, collapsed in front of us. Paramedics who were also there to show off their state-of-the-art ambulance as well as their vast knowledge, sprang into action, rushing to her aid within seconds, whisking her away on a stretcher for a black coffee drip, I expect. I suspect the word 'grounded' would have been bandied about in her house last night!

We'd been sitting on the grass when Lucas reached out and squeezed my hand for a moment. It was utterly thrilling, which sounds like a wild exaggeration and an over-the-top reaction, but I had been aching to touch him all afternoon and when it happened it sent a rush of adrenaline around my entire body, waking the grumpy stomach butterflies who, until then, had been grateful for the day off.

I was amazed that we didn't run into anyone from the Centre — yet again I suspect we are living a charmed life. Those who have affairs always end up being caught out, if not by their partners, by others who see them and blab to everyone they know until the information, like poison, finally seeps into the ears of the injured party. One way or another, we will be found out. I am making the most of him while I can. I was proud to be walking beside my beautiful man. I noticed a few second glances he received from women (and men of course!) but also noticed that he did not return them, unless it was one from me! Mmmm. I have told you before, Kevin Godley and Lol Creme, I am NOT in love, so don't you forget it. I imagine he won't be mine for long. He will choose the younger arms of another when he becomes more settled (oops, sounding ridiculously melodramatic now). Perhaps I *am* exploiting his vulnerability. A cougar — typical sexist term with predatory connotations. An older male may be called 'sugar daddy' or something similarly benevolent, not an animal on the hunt for innocent prey.

We returned home and ate curry we'd bought from a stall — delicious. More salsa dancing before bed. Fabulous again. He's incredibly attentive to my needs. He said I always wear nice 'underwears' (cute) so I told him I'd bought it in the January sales as it was cheap, then watched my nose grow two inches. I'm desperately trying to enjoy it all but can't relax. I am hyperactive, frantic, obsessed, and feel I'm about to explode. Perhaps the army should be called to either detonate or dispose of me because I'm not sure how long I can go on like this. 'She's never satisfied!' I hear you shout, from your reclining chairs. I was last night though, ladies. I was well satisfied last night!

Wednesday 24 July

Too dithery to write the diary! Been occupying my mind and idle, wicked hands with banalities like food shopping and housework. Desperate deeds call for desperate measures.

Thursday 25 July

Mouth of Tyne Festival tomorrow! Tickets for Paul Weller sold out ages ago and we were too late. It's for the best because Lucas wouldn't have been able to afford one. Undeterred, we're going along anyway to have a picnic outside Tynemouth Priory where we will be able to hear the great PW. Sam thinks my love of Paul Weller is hilarious and not in keeping with my otherwise middle of the road tastes and almost total disinterest in decent music, as she calls it. The fact that he was, and still is, a very attractive man has absolutely nothing to do with it.

Friday 26 July

Mouth of the Tyne Festival
Had a fab time tonight listening to Paul alongside the other Weller disciples who couldn't get tickets! Great atmosphere. Lucas hadn't heard of him, which is hardly surprising because in Colombia it's either salsa or other Latin American music, or American rock, apparently. Took the Metro to Tynemouth. The Priory is the perfect venue for a festival: a clifftop with a dramatic backdrop of the beautiful ruins, the sea and the sky; most atmospheric. Weather was also perfect — a warm sunny evening, light until at least half past ten. Eight of us went: Sam and Ben, Sara, Simon, Nik and two of his friends. I was much more relaxed in a group in case we saw anyone from the Centre. We had our own party on the grass outside, involving eating, dancing, and singing along to the old favourites! The hard core fans stood out from the crowd by knowing the words to his more recent songs — although not hard core enough to put themselves out to get tickets for it.

Great banter especially from Simon who was trying to impress Nik and his friends. Lucas found it hard to keep up with the jokes especially as they were delivered at the pace of a high speed train. People came a-touting tickets, but we outsiders were having such a good time that no one was interested in defecting to the inside. If you stood on the wall outside the pub you could *almost* see him on the gigantic screen. Everyone took turns and we named it Weller Wall, like Henman Hill or Murray Mound! Can't remember being so happy for a long time — apart from last week when I was alone with Lucas for the first time. Before meeting him, in my former life, I think my last brush with happiness was discovering that a lemon had hidden itself under the bags in my shopping trolley at the supermarket therefore I had inadvertently shoplifted it. I felt I had beaten the system — after worrying about the possibility of CCTV catching the errant fruit when the eagle-eyed staff trawled through the footage. 'Are you on lemon watch today, Eddie?' 'No it's your turn, mate.' 'Oh bloody hell it's so boring.' 'Well they do cost thirty pence each so it's an important job, you know.' Luckily there was no visit from the fruit police and I got away with the heist, scot free. Yes I have lived life on the edge.

Lucas didn't stay over. He has to see the legal team in the morning. I was glad because I need to make sure we don't slide into mutual dependency, for both of our sakes. Well, for mine, if truth be told. If I *am* being honest, I do find it hard to say, 'No.' I don't want 'frying pan to fire' scenario. I was dependent on one person for my happiness for too long. It was a lesson learnt the hard way. I'm feeling self-righteous, like a heavy drinker abstaining from alcohol, or someone on a fat-free diet who has resisted an offer of fish and chips. Self-righteous maybe, but nevertheless feeling deprived of something delicious.

Tuesday 30 July

Apart from the odd email and call from friends, the past few days have been unusually quiet, which suits me at the moment and keeps me out of mischief. Been sharing my time equally between guilt and happiness. I like things to be distributed fairly.

August

Thursday 1 August

Today the stark realisation dawned that, apart from the relentless pangs of guilt from professional misconduct, I am happy — or content — no, *happy* — for the first time in many years. I am not putting it all down to medication, as that kicked in a while ago and the very best thing about it is, it's not all about Lucas; I feel happier about life in general. Hoping it's not all going to crumble when this little flingette passes and I regrettably place the lid back on the box of chocolates, leaving me heartbroken as he salsas off into the sunset. I'm conscious that I have not merely broken into the second layer, but suddenly I'm more than half way through it. One thing I do know is this: I don't ever want to finish the box.

Are we living in a temporary, idyllic, summertime bubble, skipping from one fun event to the next without a care in the world, reminiscent of a holiday romance? It doesn't seem real. Perhaps, with the onset of autumn in a few weeks, the bubble may burst.

Friday 2 August

The Centre was quiet. Minika was there, not looking her usual cheerful self. She said that her application had been held up again by paperwork or rather, the lack of it, and she was dwelling on the possibility of being sent to a detention centre and deported like a criminal. It's so, so dreadful — a woman who has been kidnapped, drugged and the victim of multiple rape, could be treated like the animals who did that to her. Even one of those crimes leaves a victim scarred for life. Tried to cheer her up by buying some delicious pastries from the Turkish deli on the West Road. She appeared a little brighter by the time she left. Lucas came in towards the end of my session. Like a schoolgirl, I went bright red (becoming a habit!) and hoped Minika didn't notice. Everyone will have assumed it was a hot flush, given my age, so I probably got away with it. Hoorah for the menopause! That must be the first time in history anyone's been relieved to have the people around you *assume* you were having a hot flush! Then, as though embroiled in some sordid, clandestine affair I arranged to meet him at the park near my house in ten minutes in case anyone saw us leave together. 'It's not a crime, Lizzie,' he keeps saying. I can't help it though, because in this crime, he would be seen as the victim and I the perpetrator.

Walked around the park then drove him to Tynemouth to look at the sea. We sat in the car, like a cute little old couple would, and watched the ferry coming in from Amsterdam with its expectant, waving passengers, ready to enjoy a weekend of fun in Newcastle. Looked like they didn't have a care in the world, but those people are few and far between. A carefree existence is reserved for happy, healthy children and a few of those in the advanced stages of dementia.

He loved it and said he could watch the sea forever, coming from a city miles from the coast it was a rare treat for him. I love our impressive coastline. Like the city, I revel in showing it off to visitors — however temporary or permanent they may be; once again, time will tell. Hoping I can share more of it with Lucas. I ought to get a move on, in case he is deported without warning. The thought makes me shudder. Bought fish and chips at North Shields fish quay and raced home with them. I have a comedy sketch that plays over in my head every time I drive home from a fish and chip shop: someone driving like a maniac, through red lights shouting, 'Chips, I've got chips! Out of the way! Emergency!' Reminiscent of *The Fast Show,* there could be a police officer who stops, then escorts the driver home safely saying, in all seriousness and without any nineteen seventies double entendre, 'What is it this week madam, battered sausage?' I half-explained it to Lucas who thought it was hilarious but didn't do the driving to go with it or we'd both literally and metaphorically have had our chips!

Lolled about in true post fish and chips fashion — full to the gills, appropriately! Said he'd thought Colombian food won the prize for the most carbohydrate on one plate (sometimes rice, beans, potatoes *and* plantain, apparently) until he'd had the fish and chip experience. Watched a great documentary about lemurs. They're adorable and fascinating creatures! Their name is derived from Roman mythology: 'lemures' were ghosts or spirits. How funny! He stayed over — had lush sex — though I still felt rather full! The great thing about having a South American boyfriend (oops I wrote 'boyfriend' — he's not my boyfriend!) is that a large posterior is a desirable attribute in a woman and they even sell padded knickers in the shops there! It's a shame we have a stick-thin culture in Britain, although when you talk to men about it they usually tell you that skinny is in no way attractive. We women, conditioned from birth and later brainwashed by the media and gossip magazines, perpetuate fat phobia. We are all body dysmorphic in varying degrees. I wonder if that will change by the time you are reading this in Shady Pines. Do your younger female friends and relatives still hate the way they look and consider themselves inadequate? I desperately hope it is no longer the case.

Lucas loves the way I look — or at least he says he does. I didn't even do my secret spruce-up this morning — sorting out my hair, applying tinted moisturiser to the lines before he wakes up and the cruel light of day illuminates them, making me feel like one of those reptilian characters from *Dr Who*. No. I am becoming relaxed, too relaxed? In keeping with my reptilian relatives, I must continue to reinforce my protective shell, a guard to protect my feelings and shield my heart against breakage.

Saturday 3 August

Couldn't eat breakfast today due to the sheer volume of the fish and chips! Lucas sloped off around midday o'clock, skulking down the path as quickly as possible so as not to be seen. He thinks it's funny, all this cloak and dagger behaviour. Having been the subject of death threats and forced to flee his country, he has every right to consider everything else trivial. Nevertheless, he respects the Centre, their rules and my wish to abide by them.

Sue rang me. The school summer holiday is one of the very few times I speak to my teaching friends because they are so busy in term time and emailing is as good as it gets. She told me that Ahmed and Hannah were getting on well and were seeing each other regularly. I am so happy for them and wish it wasn't so tricky for me and Lucas. As Hannah is a churchgoer, we weren't sure exactly how far the relationship would progress, but we both speculated that as she wasn't a *fundamental* Christian, things would most likely have been taken to the next level. I'd seen Ahmed at the Centre but hadn't wanted to pry or seem like a thirteen year old by asking if he was still 'seeing' Hannah! Nor did I feel inclined to ask him his story, but Sue filled me in on that so I will document it here for historical purposes, should we one day forget how the world has treated its citizens.

Ahmed's Story

Ahmed arrived before the government's participation in a UN resolution to allow some Syrians to enter the UK without having to claim asylum, and before the mass exodus began. He travelled on a false passport via Turkey and Greece then in a series of lorries over thousands of miles, eventually and miraculously arriving in Dover. Many refugees use false documents to travel in order to reach a safe country, but they then have the problem of proving their true identity. Ahmed could prove nothing. Unable to give them contact details for his employers for fear of reprisals or in case government spies working at the newspaper office found out where he had fled to, he was simply not believed and was jailed for a year for travelling on false documents. He told me that prison was almost as terrifying as the secret filming of the government's activists he had undertaken during his job as a journalist in Syria. His English wasn't good then, unlike now. Prison had served one useful purpose in that respect — a tiny fragment of compensation for his suffering.

After he was jailed in Britain, his parents and sister fled to the countryside where they remain, as far as he knows, in hiding with relatives. He isn't even certain they are still alive. Every day and night he worried about their safety. He said it almost drove him crazy so he forced himself to stop otherwise he would have lost the will to survive prison. At first, Ahmed was beaten up on more than one occasion by fellow inmates, accused of being a terrorist. Lacking the necessary language to explain that he was a journalist opposed to the violence and terrorism of his government, he could do little else but suffer the beatings in silence and wait. Wait, until word got around the prison that this man was no terrorist, though he could be a fraudster, travelling on false documents and the like — such was the gossip.

Twelve long, arduous months later, Ahmed's name was cleared and he was released. Finally, people had been traced by his lawyers who could vouch for his identity and, given the level of conflict in Syria at the time of his release, he was granted Leave to Remain and offered a place in a hostel in Newcastle. Delighted with his new status, he soon found a job washing cars by hand. Come rain or shine or snow, exposed to the punishing, icy winds from the Arctic via Scandinavia, he felt nothing but gratitude for having been allowed to stay. This educated, highly intelligent journalist harboured no bitterness or anger for being falsely imprisoned, 'They have to do their job,' he would say.

It is a similar story for many others too. We are outraged by the treatment they receive simply for seeking shelter from persecution, be it temporary or permanent, yet they are accepting, patient, philosophical. I admire every one of them. Ahmed had seen more than enough hatred, violence and injustice in his own country to eclipse anything he would ever experience here. He came to the Centre to offer his support to others and to meet fellow Syrians. People would arrive looking bewildered, frightened and after talking to Ahmed for a couple of hours they visibly relaxed, reassured by his words of encouragement and practical advice. A remarkable, selfless man. I think he would make a perfect partner for lovely Hannah.

Thursday 8 August

Wretched today, hungover. Out with Sara last night — the two of us were overexcited and drinking quickly. I wittered on incessantly about Lucas and Sara encouraged me. Now I'm worrying about where this is all going. Think it might come crashing down around my ears, taking me with it. Sara told me to get a grip because I am now allegedly in control, much happier and relaxed than she's seen me for years, and whatever happens I will be fine, and isn't that what I am always telling her? Today I feel vile. A deluded, middle-aged-to-old woman, swanning about, professionally misconducting myself with a man whose future is precarious and who is most likely to be emotionally scarred by his recent past. Have to admit, he definitely doesn't show any signs of stress or trauma — he's astonishing.

The bottom layer of the chocolates has been pretty much devoured, leaving the few fudge ones that nobody likes. It will soon be time to discard the box and decide on the next step, if I am afforded the luxury of deciding that myself.

After all, he's been in the country for months now. The Home Office decision can't be too far away. It could come any day now and I have to be prepared. Drinking too much isn't a wise tactic.

Not a great day. If you are having a lucky dip into the diaries and choosing a day at random to read, or choosing the same date that it is in your year, then I sincerely hope it's not this one. You may want to select again.

Friday 9 August

Arrived at the Centre, where Minika suddenly hijacked me with:
'Lizzie, are you and Lucas boyfriend and girlfriend?'
I immediately blushed, in 'love-sick schoolgirl undergoing interrogation by her peers, or parents' mode, and answered, 'No!' in *the* most defensive, obviously-she-means-yes sort of way possible. For several weeks now, whenever I have played out this moment in my head, I always look quizzically at them and reply slowly, calmly and convincingly, 'No. All we do is go to a few events together, that's all. We're friends,' like an adult, *not* like a flustered fifteen-year-old full of raging hormones!

The next thing she said was even sadder and is bringing tears to my eyes as I think back to it, 'I have seen the way he looks at you. That man likes you, Lizzie; he likes you a real lot.' Then I gabbled something like, 'Sometimes we do stuff, I don't mean *do* stuff, I mean we... er ... go places sometimes. We go out together — no I don't mean we are 'going out' together, that's different, oh you know what I mean.' The whole thing must have sounded gobbledygook to a non-native English speaker and I definitely wasn't helping her to progress to First Certificate level, quite the opposite I expect. I'm sure she'll have got the message: we were, as she suspected, 'boyfriend and girlfriend', for the time being, at least.

Sunday 11 August

He emailed this morning wanting to meet up in the afternoon so we went on an urban walk — a route I devised for Jane — Leeds Jane — not long after Twat left. I did it today to banish the demons because the first time I walked it had never felt so low in my life. Well, that's not strictly true; my lowest point was earlier this year, pre anti-depressants. But at the time just after Twat left, I was hurting; a raw, newly-wounded, acute pain. The not-yet-sunk-in kind where your stomach and heart reflect the agony, but your head is in a fuzzy, aching, on-another-planet state. Absolutely horrendous. I remember going through the motions of the walk, on a particularly windy day. It was as though I were in a film — I could hear the critics commenting on how the setting, the landscape, and weather depict the mood of the protagonist; how the scenes portraying the demise of industry in the region are analogous to her relationship with her estranged husband, having declined to a point of distinction blah blah and more arty blah. And so they continued, on and on and on. Poor Jane, she must have been put off the place (and me) for life that day; she's never been back. I ought to contact her and tell her I am semi-normal again — hmm, perhaps not quite yet.

Today was altogether a different day — sun reflecting off the bridges, Quayside — its marvellous, vibrant self, river glistening. Ouseburn — bustling with vitality, new businesses, rehearsal rooms, garages, reclaimed furniture centres, artists' studios galore, a real ale pub and the gorgeous City Farm. What more could anyone ask for? Lucas said he thought this was the real heart of the city, not the shopping centre, the football stadium or even Grey Street with its theatre and neoclassical architecture. No, he loves the Ouseburn. He said he would like to live there if he could. I was stupidly excited and my mind started racing, fantasizing about living there with him … idiot! I looked over at him and his beautiful brown eyes were glazed over — was he thinking the same? Was he reminiscing about Colombia, perhaps? Or was he merely berating himself for saying something that could be misconstrued and later thrown back in his face as 'leading me on'? Who knows? After winning a skirmish with my emotions, I took control of my delinquent head before I spoilt the remainder of the walk and we wandered back through Jesmond Dene. It's a perfect mix of natural and managed space. AND it's got animals to stroke! Never been a fan of the term 'petting zoo' — it doesn't sit comfortably and conjures up all sorts of images I'd rather not have in my head. Pets Corner is a far safer name.

I told Lucas about the time I took Sam to Pets Corner when a man was joking around with his young son saying, 'I'll put you in there, mind,' dangling him over the pot-bellied pigs' pen. The boy, older than Sam, was understandably freaked out by the very thought and began to wail until he was whisked away to safety. Sam, conversely, thinking that this was a valid option which also sounded like pure heaven, asked me, 'Can I go in with them?' That's ma girl! Frightened of nothing and no one, neither the four nor the two-legged variety.

Lucas didn't stay over. Maybe he is psychic and I scared him off with my thoughts about him living here long term. Maybe he's afraid of becoming too involved. Maybe he no longer fancies me.

Wednesday 14 August

Was almost coming to terms with the possibility of Sunday being my last clandestine meeting with Lucas, when he emailed about going out again next weekend! I have the perfect event: the Mela festival! Excited but trying to keep it all in check. Listen to me — not doing that well am I? I think house-training an elephant would be simpler!

Friday 16 August

Lucas dropped in to Centre so we could make the whispered arrangements about Sunday. It saved him having to queue for computers but it was bloody nerve-racking, especially as it was busy. Not sure about all this cloak and dagger stuff. It's not *me*.

Monday 19 August

Mela

I love the Mela! Newcastle celebrates its South Asian community through this delightful festival. Not only is it a lively, colourful event in itself but it fills my heart with joy to see the white families of the area flocking to support the event: we are multicultural and proud of it, come and enjoy the fun. Fabric stalls with every vivid colour under the sun, bejewelled clothing in fine, floaty silky fabrics. Bangles galore and the food stall (cue Sara) OMG! It was curry heaven — again bright, brimming with colour and exuding the most delicious smells, leading us all into temptation! Oh Lord! The fabulous dancing and music: Bollywood and bhangra, full of vitality and passion, mirroring how I feel at the moment; a perfect complement to the clothing and accessories. Many of the women wear traditional clothing for the event: their best salwar kameez and saris, reserved for special occasions. Others in their usual, western, trendy clothes, again demonstrating how multicultural they are.

Lucas said there is a 'Black and White' festival in Pasto, Colombia, to celebrate the different cultures: Indigenous, Spanish and Afro- Colombian cultures. It sounds like an equally colourful but, like most things Latin American, whole lot wilder event! Ate curry on the grass and watched the dancers. Gorgeous! As ever, slightly nervous about being clocked by someone from the Centre. We may have been, of course, unbeknownst to us. On a multicultural high (not only legal but also free!) we came back, opened wine and fell asleep on the sofa. Woke up in the middle of the night, dragged ourselves up the stairs and flopped into bed. Then I remembered to remove my mascara in the nick of time to avoid lemur/ghost eyes. Too tired for anything but sleep, I snuggled in and fell asleep with my head nestling against his back, my arm wrapped tightly around him.

Tuesday 20 August

Not good — despite the fun we had yesterday, and this morning. Had a quick email from him in the afternoon thanking me for the wonderful day and night BUT no mention of meeting up. No plan.

Watched lots of TV as a distraction then went to bed feeling very low. It's an up-and-downy, roller-coastery, and all things undulating affair, that's for sure.

Thursday 22 August

I need to strengthen my shield, reinforce the barriers, thicken my invisible shell of protection, for I am becoming too relaxed, too complacent about the situation. I can smell change in the air, and it's not the chill breeze of autumn. I want it to last. I'm not the type who welcomes change and I hate the thought of summer ending, nights lengthening — although the 'glass half empty' brigade have been cheerfully reminding us of that since the twenty-first of June. Like a child might say, I want summer to last all year, as it does on the Equator. I would have to use gallons of sunscreen, being as white as a uPVC door. People have tried and failed to convince me that I would miss the seasons and the changes they bring, aka cold and wet weather, and how very boring it would be to have heat all year round. That's a barrow load of drivel. Bring it on: twelve months of summer, forget about the skin cancer — although, of course, I would mind very much if I had it and I apologise for sounding flippant.

It's Lucas. He knows his decision for Leave to Remain is fairly imminent. I can sense him preparing for the worst, having received very positive feedback so far from the lawyer who's told him several times she's had success with the other two Colombian trade unionists she represented. Lucas has been in contact with one of them, now living in London, to reassure him of the positive aspects of their asylum-seeking experiences and no doubt share some negative ones. I shouldn't be so maudlin, but it's because I've had *such* a wonderful time this summer, with Lucas playing a significant part in it, though I'm loathe to admit it. I happened upon a quote from Mary Shelley's *Frankenstein*:

I have love in me the likes of which you can scarcely imagine and rage the likes of which you would not believe.

It struck a chord. Have I created something which is soon to become beyond my control?

Friday 23 August

Didn't see Lucas at the Centre today. He's avoiding me, I know it. How could I have been so stupid? I can't bring myself to put my conflicting feelings into words. They are knotted and twisted like chains, each pulling at the other, tightening all the while in an effort to become untangled, ordered, and replaced neatly.

Saturday 24 August

8.00 a.m. Woke up early worrying about Minika — will she tell anyone about me and Lucas? It's been two weeks now and I haven't been summoned to explain myself to Rob, the Centre manager, so there's no reason to think she will spill any Colombian coffee beans now. Not a joking matter. She would never do it out of malice, only human interest, or by mistake. Perhaps she'll ask the others if they've noticed anything about the two of us. I should have confessed all my terrible sins, confided in her so she can appreciate why people mustn't start to wonder about us. Must speak to her and beg her not to tell anyone. I'm sure she's trustworthy. Minika's honest, a woman of great integrity, which is why she might feel it her duty to tell someone. No. Maybe I won't. But she likes both of us so I can't imagine her wanting to destroy a friendship... oh I don't know!

YES, I will tell her.

Sunday 25 August

Fanfare: Lucas emailed! He's seeing the lawyers on Friday and they expect to have heard about his claim by then. He wants to come round on Thursday. The Last Supper? If Leave to Remain is refused, he could be whisked off to a detention centre in a matter of days in case he tries to disappear. It's so tempting — my mind's doing overtime, whirring around. I know Scotland well. There are places there where you could be totally anonymous, and the immigration police would never trace you. My friend, who owns a tiny cottage on the Western Isles, is a sound bloke who could be trusted not to say anything. But a life on the run? In hiding, looking over your shoulder, lies, lies, and more lies. A new identity for Lucas and perhaps for me, should anyone let the cat out of the bag. Dearest diary reader — I'd give anything to be in your position, knowing what's to become of him, of me, of us.

At one time I'd have gone to a psychic, a medium — to see what the future held. When I think back to all the rubbish they spouted, not one iota of it came true! Are you allowed to sue these people or at least claim your money back? Once, Mum and I went together to a psychic who had a supposedly good reputation. I went in first and came out as per usually unimpressed while Mum was raving about her session, 'She's incredible! She said I was 'surrounded by needles'!' 'That's because I told her you were diabetic,' I told her, bursting her bubble and making the woman look even more like a charlatan. Derren Brown will tell you all you need to know about psychic mediums or are they medi*a*? It's a good read and will save you an awful lot of money in the real future.

I digress, on purpose. Avoidance tactics to save me from confronting the truth. Worst case scenario: he could be deported. Second worst case scenario: he's granted Leave to Remain and moves to London. Third worst case scenario: he's granted Leave to Remain and wants to stay in Newcastle.

I have a feeling the second worst is the most likely because:
a) I am an optimist
b) I'm not *that* much of an optimist

He's been talking a lot, lately, about the sizable Colombian and Latin American community in London and about the range of great salsa venues, bands, groups, societies, and refugee support centres I know he'd be involved with should it all go according to plan. The *plan* being the one he's hatched in his head and concealed from me for now! Paranoid? I don't think so. I have lived long enough now to read between lines and deduce what is going on in someone's mind. What's more, I do it free of charge.

Wednesday 28 August

Had a great day yesterday! Met Hilary for lunch then spontaneous cocktails; a perfect combination and an ideal distraction — the best laugh I've ever had with her. Haven't seen a drunken Hilary for many years. She was always driving, living out in the sticks as she does. It was perfect when her kids were younger, but now that she's decided to live a little, it's a right royal pain in the arse. She'd got a lift into town with her husband, Miserable Jeff, whose face was an absolute picture when he picked her up later. I bundled her, giggling like a schoolgirl, into the car. Nevertheless, Miserable Jeff has an important function to perform. Apart from taxiing, he serves as a stark reminder of why I'm so much better off being single.

I recognise that look: disapproving, jealous that the wife is having a good time for once without him. Twat did a good line in sour grapes, with a canny knack of negating any fun you may have had with one tut and a roll of the eyes. Naturally, he was on to a loser every time because it would inevitably provoke an argument. Bringing down the mood of an alcohol-fuelled, stressed, unhappily married woman is never a wise move.

Poor Hilary, I hope she didn't get a hard time from slapped-arse face. It's a long drive to the back of beyond. However, I can satisfy your curiosity as to why, apart from alcohol, the afternoon was such fun: Hilary (who can be a drain) was introduced to the 'Out of...' game Debs and I used to play. It was HILarious! I've never in my life seen Hilary laugh till she can't breathe — sheer delight to witness! I kicked it off with, 'Out of David Cameron, Tony Blair and (mixing it up a bit) Evan Davies from the BBC, who would you choose to do it with?' The ensuing debates were as funny and heated as they were in the old days and, as the choices became more and more bizarre, the tears streamed down our mascara-streaked faces. With the cocktails flowing, I forced her to make a list of the top five men (in order of lushness) from our friends or acquaintances' husbands or partners (including exes). That was funny enough, but far more amusing was the bottom five list (in order of foulness)! If anyone was earwigging they'd have heard Hilary saying in an agitated tone, 'I *know* they both had vile breath but Nigel's was slightly less pungent than Pete's, even though he was more boring so he's *got* to stay at number four. I'm not budging on that one!' Later on they'd have witnessed me, almost yelling, 'I can't BELIEVE you'd choose Ian Beale from *Eastenders* over Tyrone from *Coronation Street*!' That raised a few passing eyebrows.

Without a doubt it was the best day I've ever spent with Hilary and, after a brief update on the Lucas situation, it kept my mind off him for most of the day. Alone again with my thoughts — at least the afternoon drinking means I'm about to fall asleep. Oh damn! Meant to do, 'Donald Trump or George W. Bush?' Will save it for next time.

Thursday 29 August

BIG NEWS — I TOLD MINIKA! I called into the Centre with an excuse about donations and took her out for coffee. She was so sweet and understanding, though I didn't tell her he's stayed over on several occasions. I told her we are very close and that I suppose I am (or was?) having some sort of very-much-against-the-rules relationship with him. I swore her to secrecy, poor woman, as if she hasn't got enough on her plate. She was encouraging, to the point of gushing and said we were a 'beautiful couple'. Hard to cope with in the light of what could happen with Lucas's case tomorrow. I told her I know how unprofessional it was as a volunteer and she laughed, 'Rules, so many rules. Some are made for breaking.' I thanked her, but feel no less guilty. As I used to tell the kids at school, 'Despite what you think, rules are there for a reason: either for your own safety or out of respect for others. They're not created with the sole purpose of to making your lives a misery.' This one is no exception — although Lucas himself has tried his utmost to convince me that I'm not exploiting his situation, or being disrespectful, I feel my emotional security is in danger of being compromised.

He came over to eat in the evening and arrived holding flowers, 'One pound from the Grainger Market!' he announced triumphantly. I made a roast dinner — it was feeling more and more like The Last Supper. Although I've never noticed chicken, gravy, and Yorkshire puddings in Leonardo's painting, I maybe ought to have made something low key. He didn't stay, but I couldn't resist asking if he wanted to adjourn to the bedroom. I'd resolved not to do that, in case I obsessed about it possibly being the last time and spoilt it, but I couldn't stop my greedy self from having one more dip into the box of delights, which is looking rather depleted these days. I'm acutely aware of its limited shelf life.

Lucas was clearly nervous about tomorrow so I tackled the subject head on, 'Will you stay in Newcastle if you are granted Leave to Remain?' He looked uncomfortable and said, 'I don't know Lizzie. I'm not allowing myself to dream like that, in case my claim is rejected.' A politician's answer, but I didn't force the issue. That *would* be unprofessional. God, why couldn't I have stuck to the rules and spurned his advances from the outset rather than allow myself to be flattered? Look at you now, Moffitt. You're pathetic. Rules are, after all, there for a reason. I said a prayer for him, in case God exists.

Friday 30 August

Thank God, or rather the Home Office, as the decision had already been made before my insurance policy style of praying — HE CAN STAY! No worrying for five years! I absolutely can't believe it, nor can he. He emailed me from the Centre with the great news — I was in manic email-checking mode (ugh a horrible flashback to the dark days of dating and depression). He told me to make an excuse to call at the Centre as they would be having the customary modest party and said, 'You *must* come, Lizzie, to celebrate with me!' Confession: after the initial euphoria I had a feeling of dread. Where will he choose — London or Newcastle? I know I've been telling myself he is merely on loan, passing through, but at this moment I don't want him to go. I really don't. GET A GRIP! Mum's voice came into my head, as it does when I need help in a crisis, 'Come on Elizabeth, you're made of strong stuff. It'll all work out in the end and you will be fine. You'll see to that.'

So, I went to the party under the pretext of asking if they need help next week, as two volunteers are on holiday. Very difficult to know what sort of congratulatory hug to give Lucas so that it wouldn't look all too comfortable and natural, like I did it several times a week, which I do! Minika gave me a knowing smile, understanding the awkwardness of the situation and Rob made a lovely speech. He said how he appreciates that Lucas might be tempted down to London by the large Latin American community but, apart from Rob's beloved Chelsea football team, life in Newcastle is much better and we don't want to lose him. I had to choke back the tears while everyone cheered and laughed. Strong stuff? I'll need to do better than this.

Sam called round after work. I'd texted her and the others with the good news. They were all so supportive, which was lovely, although I know they'll all be thinking, 'What now?' Protective as ever, Sam urged me to push him into an answer about his intentions: are they honourable? Defensively, I explained that I was sure he doesn't know yet what he'll do as he hadn't wanted to think beyond today.

'Oh come on, Mum. He must have an idea,' she sniffed. Tables turned again: mother questioned by daughter who claims to know the workings of every man's mind at the tender age of twenty-three. Not sure I'm comfortable with this.

Feeling the need to restore the natural order of things, again I resorted to my serious, teacher's voice tactic, 'Sam, it doesn't matter either way.' Also had to employ my drama skills to sound nonchalant, but I think I got away with it. Mother is finally back in control of her feelings and her life. Doesn't need lecture from daughter. Daughter feels secure being put back in place. Everyone can relax.

When she'd gone I opened wine. No email from Lucas. Why would there be? He'd left the Centre before me, had to go back to the lawyers for paperwork and they'd kindly invited him for a drink to celebrate. They're a remarkable bunch of people who work tirelessly, beyond the call of duty, for the asylum seekers they represent. He's going to buy a phone tomorrow. Says he can't do without one any longer and has a small amount of money left that he brought with him. It should make things much easier for us, or maybe not. I might be in paranoid text-checking mode in place of email-checking mode. In need of a dose of my very best medicine, I took a deep breath and delved into the diary box.

Flicked through to the thirtieth of August in my eighteenth year. My first driving test! I have struck diary gold with my first attempt! I was laughing even before starting it, as I have dined out on this story many times. Having recently completed what was almost literally a six-week crash course of driving lessons then persuading anyone and everyone with a licence to take me out to practise, I decided I was more than ready for my test. Uber-confident, I took it in my mum's car and told her I'd ring her from the test centre payphone if I failed so she could come and drive me home. I was certain it wouldn't be necessary and pictured myself pulling up outside the house, tooting and waving, waiting to be congratulated by the proud parents. I knew I'd made a couple of minor errors in the test, including a massive swerve, rather than applying the brakes, to avoid a cat but I thought I'd acted decisively and therefore wouldn't be penalised. Turning smugly to the examiner, I was mortified to hear the word 'failed' somewhere in the sentence before a long list of mistakes were read out, including the apparently 'dangerous' swerve.

He got out of the car, expecting me to follow him into the office to call my mum and also to collect the said long list of near-fatal errors so I drove off! Being a good driver, I checked my mirror and saw him standing, open-mouthed, getting smaller and smaller with each check. Yes, I drove the four miles home illegally, through a built-up area, and the examiner never reported it — those were the good old seventies for you! When I was almost home I picked up Debs who lived around the corner and had passed her test so she could sit in with me as we drew up to the house. It was ages before we could compose ourselves to break the disappointing news to Mum and Dad; we were laughing so much it was worth failing just for the craic!

Thinking of that examiner's horrified face in my rear view mirror, I went to bed giggling and resolved to email Debs tomorrow to tell her that today was the thirty-seventh anniversary of the driving test failure story!

Saturday 31 August

Woke up with a sensation of impending doom. Shouldn't 'catastrophize' as Simon would say — it's never been in my nature to do so but having experienced things beyond my control: divorce and depression, I am now fully aware of the nasty little surprises life hurls at you when you're least expecting them. Lucas wants to meet up tomorrow. Had to distract myself so arranged to meet Simon (the best man for the job) this afternoon, and he didn't disappoint!

Met at Monument and caught a bus to Fenham. He wouldn't tell me what he had planned but by the self-satisfied grin on his face I knew he'd come up with the goods: The Cat Café — my idea of paradise! I'd been meaning to go since it opened as it's to support the Westgate Ark cat homing charity — he knows I love cats but haven't had one since pre-Twat days. Should've realised then that it was a doomed relationship. Never mind that, there are real, live, beautiful, cuddly, cute cats scampering around this heavenly place (not in the kitchen or on the tables, before you lot go all 'health and safety' on me). An adorable grey kitten called Grace clambered onto my knees and purred away gloriously while I stroked her. If I had to make a list, I would say that this was therapy number one, with diaries coming a close second at number two. Simon, of course, had to spoil it by saying they probably 'cull them' after six months when they're too big to be cute and bring in a load of newer, younger moggy models! He's incorrigible!

Couldn't avoid talking about the Lucas situation, which was fine as I realised I'm getting increasingly prepared for the moving to London scenario. 'It's hardly Colombia, Lizzie. Three hours on a train, that's nowt!' I was told, in no uncertain terms, 'He'll probably want to stay here if he's got any sense. It's so expensive to live there now, and he's not going to have a high-powered job, is he?' he said, reassuringly. Came back feeling thoroughly relaxed after my feline fix. Didn't even feel the need for wine. Not looking forward to tomorrow. A new month, a new chapter. It could go either way.

September

Sunday 1 September

Oh my God — the bombshell has been dropped!
You must, dear readers, have been thinking, 'Just you wait, Elizabeth!' You didn't see that one coming, did you?' I am in shock, utter shock. My head is spinning and both heart and stomach are doing some sort of complicated gymnastic routine. Here it is:
He's going to London (boo).
He wants me to go with him (hurray).
I am in complete turmoil. Can't possibly do that at my age — can I? Daren't mention it to Sam. Spoke to Sara who screamed down the phone, 'Aaaah that's lush!' Lucas and I were at Tynemouth, walking along the promenade above the beach when he said, 'Come with me Lizzie. It will be an adventure, a new life for both of us.' I'd told him before that I always regret not living in London for a few years, but I meant when I was in my twenties, not fifties! I told him I can't go. It's impossible. My life is here, and that's when he said IT, 'But I love you, Lizzie.' I fought back the tears at that point and told him it was the wind making my eyes water. I didn't ask him to come home with me as I knew I'd be easily persuaded by his charm offensive. I would end up saying, 'Yes, yes, yes of course I'll come with you,' and regret it in the morning. Told him I need time to think.

Monday 2 September

This calls for another list.

For moving to London:

- Always wanted to live there — experience the London buzz.
- Can video-call Sam and friends.
- Three hours on a train.
- A new chapter of my life.
- I would be with Lucas — should be at top of list!
- Could be fun going to salsa clubs/meeting new people.
- Could live in a multicultural area and learn Spanish properly.
- I could come back if I didn't like it.
- You have one life. It's an opportunity and we might live happily ever after.

Against moving to London:

- London is expensive — quality of life?
- I will miss Sam and my friends terribly.
- Train travel is expensive.
- Do I want to jump in with both feet?
- Too old to go to salsa clubs and they might all be much younger than me.
- There are too many people there.
- Could I face the heartache if it all went wrong?

The more I write, the harder it becomes. 'For' is winning on quantity, but it's the quality that counts. I'm allowed to make the rules.

Tuesday 3 September

More angst. Told Sam. The words, 'You're not going are you?' said in a 'you must me mad' tone of voice, actually made me want to go immediately! I suppose that's the rebel in me. It's strangely comforting to know that I still have a rebellious streak, simmering below the surface, that hasn't been burnt out by the anti-depressants. When I told her I hadn't decided, she softened and revealed that it was because she'd miss me so much and not because she thought I'd lost my mind. That made it all the more difficult.

I've spent my whole life living in one place, with a tinge of regret for not having travelled, apart from on holiday. Now's my chance, before I really *will* be too old. Lucas plans to teach Spanish and salsa dancing and also study to convert his teaching qualifications to be able to teach in primary schools here. I could do some home tutoring if I needed more money than my pension provided me with. We could rent a very modest, one-bed flat for the same rent as my three-bed house would fetch here, I think. Not great, but all part of a new life. I could even do supply teaching — or maybe not. We're having a few days apart, which is hard but essential if I'm going to reach a clear-headed decision or wean myself off him if I reject his offer. Don't fancy the latter. I am not as tough-talking as my words would suggest.

Wednesday 4 September

Met Sara. 'Why can't he stay here?' was her reaction and my sentiments exactly, but to admit it isn't helping the situation. I explained that there are so many more opportunities for him there: people are constantly coming and going so if someone has moved to London for a couple of years, teaching Spanish or salsa to get by, they hand over their students or classes to the next person i.e. Lucas, when they leave — everyone is happy!

After that, it turned into, 'Okay, then you *must* go! Isn't it exactly what you need? A new start, new opportunities. Let's face it, you've been struggling with early retirement until now. They have refugee centres there don't they? You might meet someone else!' Cheeky madam! What if he wants to go back to Colombia in a few years' time? Sara trumped that with, 'Life's full of 'what ifs' but you have to go for it sometimes and cross those bridges if, not when, you come to them.' Aaaagh! I'm no further forward. Every time I'm persuaded by Sara, I see Sam's sad face saying, 'You have to do whatever makes you happy, Mum.' Then Simon's voice pops up, 'One life, Lizzie-Lou. One life.'

Friday 6 September

Head ready to explode but feeling better after the Centre. Lucas dropped by and mentioned the Great North Run. Arranged a rendezvous at my house on Sunday to go and watch the start of the race. I knew he was dying to ask if I'd made a decision but I ushered him out before anyone overheard us.

Sunday 8 September

Great North Run

The run is one of the most heart-warming, restore-your-faith-in-human-nature-despite-what-the-nasty-newspapers-want-us-to-think events you will ever witness. I live near the start line and, although the participants don't need our encouragement quite so early on in the race, you feel like you've done your civic duty and contributed in some way, been an integral part of the whole thing and earned your bacon butty that you guzzle from the comfort of your own sofa, watching the rest of it on TV.

Lucas was astounded by the amount of runners — over fifty thousand — many of whom are running for a charity close to their hearts. A cause to support, for a relative, a friend, a colleague or themselves. Having something to be grateful for, someone to thank, a reason to run. People in wheelchairs, blind people with guides, people on crutches, Jarra Jim — an extraordinary man in his nineties. One man carrying a fridge, another, wrestling with a kitchen sink! How can they possibly survive thirteen miles of that? Then there are countless costumed characters: chickens, pandas, Minnie and Mickey mice, camels, giraffes, bees, butterflies, and bears. Superheroes of every hue: Hulks (green) Spidermen (red). There is nothing more incongruous than an elderly Spiderman — it messes with your head. Those people deserve an extra cheer running in the heat of a nylon costume fashioned from faux fur or similar man-made, sweat-inducing, non-breathable material.

As a teacher, Lucas was particularly impressed by the children who line the route, spotting the names of the runners on their bibs as they approach and shouting, 'Come on Bill! You can do it Annie!' as the grateful recipients of the encouragement pass by, sometimes with a high-five of appreciation. Then the cynic in me kicks in and says, 'They'll be sick of the high-fives by the time they reach the Tyne Bridge!' Dropping coins into their collection buckets is also double-edged: it's actual cruelty, burdening them with small change to lug around the course at this stage. Isn't the race hard enough without a ton of copper weighing you down, lulling the enthusiastic collector into a false sense of security as they assume the change is silver? 'Six pounds forty-two pence for all that pain? That's me finished!' On the other hand, every little helps.

Further down the line, on the Gateshead side, the generosity is magnified: people come from their houses bearing oranges, water, sponges to spur on the flagging, rapidly dehydrating majority. The South Shields kids are much more pragmatic, squirting their water pistols and spray guns to cool them and wash away the sweat. We are privileged to host such a spectacle, a nationally acclaimed event. Lucas loved the camaraderie and sense of community it espouses. He laughed hysterically when I told him about my friend, David, who caught one of the buses back after the run and reported, 'It stank of sweat and Ralgex. It was revolting!'

Went for a drink at one of the Ouseburn pubs later in the afternoon and saw a few people sporting their medals. They were walking, or staggering, their knees no longer fit for purpose, like they'd had a Paula Radcliffe type of accident but hadn't managed to stop en route. A salutary reminder of why I have never been, and will never be, brave enough to enter the Great North Run.

Told Lucas he must go back to his hostel because I hadn't yet decided what to do. It was painful to watch him walk away, particularly after such a fabulous day, but it had to be done.

Tuesday 10 September

With my nearest and dearest sending my head into turbospin over the past few days, I decided I needed a walk along the Quayside, where the rusty old boat, Tuxedo Princess, a floating nightclub, used to be. Must dig out a diary documenting one of those nights of pure, wall-to-wall laughter on the revolting (revolving) dance floor — enough to give any self-respecting Health and Safety Officer the heebie-jeebies.

'No, you can't ban the revolving dance floor!'
'But twenty-three people in the last month alone have twisted or broken legs, arms, ankles, and wrists.'

'Look, man, they're Geordies, they're hard and they divvent care. Close it doon and you'll have a real revolution on your hands!'

'Canny pun, mate. Aye. Suppose ya reet.'

And so it stayed, until the boat rusted away around it, well into the nineties.

I flicked through a few diaries but wasn't lucky this time. I wanted to find an account of a frequent occurrence on the boat — something akin to a David Attenborough programme. A lone male, separated from the pack, fancying his chances on the revolting dance floor, would make his move on one of the females. Soon afterwards he'd find himself encircled by the protective females in her group who would home in and dance around, taunting him mercilessly to 'Dancing Queen' or 'YMCA', until the poor lad was embarrassed into fleeing the dance floor, scarred for life.

I miss Lucas, but feel calmer today, not being swayed by the arguments of others, first one way, then the next. I will toss a coin. 'What?' I hear you shout, a little too loudly for the other residents' liking, 'Is that how she decided what to do? She made a life-changing decision on the toss of a coin?' No, friends. Do not fear. Coin-tossing is a barometer for your feelings. You toss the coin and say, 'Heads I go to London, tales I stay.' Coin lands on tales — *then* you'll know which way to decide: if you're disappointed and wanted it to be heads, then you must go. If you're relieved, then you must stay. I tossed the coin. It was heads. I was happy. I've made the decision — I'm going. I must be mad. Oh, to be in your shoes, or slippers, knowing how it all pans out. Did I do the right thing?

Wednesday 11 September

8.45 a.m. Woke up wondering if I should change my mind and re-toss that coin. NO! But the thought of anyone at the Centre finding out fills me with dread. I can't tell them yet. Shit, more secrecy. Never been one for procrastinating, I tend to get on and do it. I'm not sure about this – but then I never will be until I try it. GET ON WITH IT, MOFFITT!

Hilary called in reply to my general text I'd sent when Lucas had his claim approved — old news. Had to tell her I wasn't sure yet what was happening — after all I couldn't have Hilary being the first to know my news, before Sam and Lucas! Need help and affirmation before breaking the news to Sam and co. I'm turning to the trusty old diaries in my hour of need. My younger, more confident self will invigorate me and rekindle my sense of adventure, hopefully. It will also serve as an ideal delaying tactic before telling the others!

I knew the very one to search for: Mallorca with Chris. When we were twenty-five my great friend Chris went to teach in an international school in Mallorca. I went with her for the first two weeks, ostensibly as a luggage mule but in reality it was the perfect excuse for a wild holiday. She had to find her own accommodation so instead of doing the sensible thing and booking a hotel through a travel agent, pre-internet days, we, in our twenty-five year old wisdom, decided that Mallorca was full of hotels and pitched up with the world's biggest suitcase we dubbed 'the house on wheels' and another enormous contender for the title. After hauling them from one full hotel to the next for hours on end and attracting a lot of attention — due not only to our age but to the ridiculously oversized luggage — we adjourned to a bar. There, an older (thirtysomething) guy took pity on us and we ended up staying in his hotel room while he slept on the floor! When eyebrows were understandably raised among the people we later met up with from the school, we assured them that he had reported there being a, 'Ring of fire round that bed!'

The next day, one of the teachers' friends (later renamed Mark the Shark) sorted us out with a lovely studio apartment which turned out to be sublet — to the fury of the owner! It was an eventful few weeks when many life lessons were learned! A true adventure, and fun to boot! After a few pages documenting where we beached, ate, drank, danced, and drank more, who we'd snogged and who we fancied, I got the message: go for it, girl! In the (almost) words of both Gary Barlow and Lulu, relight that fire!

Friday 13 September

Centre was, thankfully, uneventful. Met Sam in the Bridge Hotel, a lovely old pub overlooking the river, to tell her my decision. It was traumatic.

As soon as she saw me she said, 'You're going aren't you?' I immediately burst into tears. How stupid. I didn't want it to be like that at all, but maybe it was for the best, because Sam was so lovely and encouraging — contrary to what I was expecting. It's lovely when your own children surprise you like that. 'You mustn't worry about me, Mum. I'm a big grown-up you know. And I want lots of weekends in London with you. We can do the shows and sights and you might finally learn to make video-calls!' She also added that since I'd met Lucas I was swearing much less, which must be a good sign! How funny. I hadn't even noticed that!

I feel thoroughly emotionally drained, but it was a huge relief to have the seal of approval from my amazing daughter. I explained about having to give it a try and how I ought to take the opportunity, and that Lucas had told me he loved me. She asked if I loved him, and I was taken aback because the guards and shields have been doing their job most ably, therefore I've never allowed myself to ponder the question. 'I think so,' I replied, lamely, hoping Lucas wouldn't be the next to ask me that.

Text from Sara: I heard your news! You're a dark horse, Lizzie Moffitt! Made up for you, girl. xx

Can't wait to tell him on Sunday, not tomorrow, as I want another night to sleep on it. Lizzie Moffitt: fifty-five and three quarters, upping sticks and moving to London. A new chapter. Very nervous. What I do know is: I most probably am, secretly *in* love or I wouldn't be going. And to be *in* love, Lol Creme, is a more precarious position by far.

Saturday 14 September

10.00 a.m. A BAD START.
Wonder when I'll stop waking up in a panic about this! Need to come to terms with it. Decided I mustn't tell the Centre I'm moving away until I am about to leave. Deceitful, I know, but I can't risk them kicking me out. Also if they find out about me and Lucas they might get in touch with other refugee support centres and I could be on a national blacklist of unsuitable volunteers who behave inappropriately and flout the rules. Or shall I leave right now? Can't decide on the best course of action. Don't want to let them down or (selfishly) stop going. What would I say? 'I've too much on at the moment,'? I'd sound like the world's flakiest woman. 'Sorry everyone, one day a week has proved too much for me, with all my coffee and lunch engagements.' I don't think so! Will have to stick with it and brazen it out, as Gran would have said.

Sunday 15 September

A far better day! Lucas came round to eat last night. I started to doubt myself yet again but as soon as I saw him my stomach told me I was doing the right thing: the butterfly squad made their presence felt. Or is it because he's so beautiful? He looked nervous, like a defendant awaiting the jury's verdict. He was over the moon when I told him the unanimous decision — a relief because our few days apart had allowed demons to creep in again, making me wonder if he'd changed his mind and would be looking forward to a rejection! Not so. He was so happy and appreciated the enormity of the decision, saying, 'You are an incredible woman, Lizzie. I promise to make you very, very happy.' Then launched into Spanish which I couldn't understand a word of but sounded very appealing and sexy nonetheless! Must learn more of the language as part of my new life. He stayed over — gorgeous. I might finally allow myself the luxury of getting used to this.

Tuesday 17 September

Early pizza with a hyperactive, overexcited Simon! He's already asking to come down and stay on a sofa, quipping, 'Unless it's your bed, of course,' knowing the deal in London. A pensioner and a refugee won't be living anywhere near the centre of town. I can't quite believe I'm doing this. Simon's insisting on helping me declutter, to make the house remotely rentable. Naturally, everyone wants to know the plan — when, when, when? We're thinking of going after Christmas. New Year will be a good time to let the house, apparently. Lucas would go down sooner to find work and somewhere for us to live. As it's almost October, we haven't got that much time. Ugh! Shudder of fear runs down spine. I envy your knowledge, dear readers and residents of Shady Pines, to be in the privileged position of either remembering or having read next year's diary to see what's in store for me. I wish I could have a glimpse. Does it all end in tears, I wonder?

Simon buoyed me up no end. You need an over-exuberant friend at a time like this. Not sure if Hilary will have the same effect. After all, she might, try to make me see sense, and succeed.

Friday 20 September

Have had a week of dentist (yuk), making sure all friends know the news, and a permanently churning stomach. Lucas came on Wednesday (yum) and made sure I hadn't changed my mind by salsa dancing around the lounge, which resulted in my insisting that he stayed the night!

The Centre was, thankfully, quiet today. I feel like I am harbouring a guilty secret and that it must be written all over my face. Michael was there, having a coffee. It's the first time I'd seen him on his own since his claim was approved so I felt it more appropriate than before to ask about his circumstances and journey to Britain.

Michael's Story

Of all the refugees whose stories have been shared with me, Michael undertook the longest and most arduous journey of them all. Two years in transit, fleeing from religious persecution by the Eritrean government, along with thousands of his neighbours and members of the church community. His story is remarkable, particularly considering his fifty-six years and the conditions he endured along the way. Almost three years ago, Michael, his wife and two teenage sons, along with his younger neighbour's family, were rounded up after attending church one day and taken to the military prison. His crime: being of the wrong faith — a Christian.

Weeks went by without any information, any charges being read to them and certainly no trial. Gradually, rumours, later to be confirmed as facts, spread around the prison about arbitrary executions of Christian prisoners. In an extraordinary feat of bravery combined with good luck, he and the neighbour escaped through a hole in the fence when they were outside digging up the iron-like ground — their routine hard labour. They managed to reach the city and hide out with Michael's relatives for a few weeks. Their intention was to seek help from the international community by publicising what was happening and secure the release of the prisoners. Tragically, before they could achieve this, the dreadful news came: broadcast by the government-controlled media as a warning to other potential escapees from the military prison, Michael and the neighbour learned that their families had been executed. How they must have felt after that, is beyond the realms of imagination. He began slowly to come to terms with it after discovering that every one of the remaining prisoners of faith had also been executed shortly afterwards. The unbearable guilt of assuming it was a direct result of the escape was alleviated to some extent, although the pain remained as unbearable as ever.

Following the news, Michael and the neighbour fled to Sudan, spending ten months in a refugee camp on the border there. What the world fails to realise is that in some of these camps, human traffickers prey on the vulnerable and many are promised transport to Italy via Libya but are kidnapped en route and held to ransom, sold to other gangs or even traded as slaves. Luckily, due to his age, Michael wasn't a target, but his neighbour would always hide when the gangs raided the camps, looking for young men and women to take. Eventually, having no other option, they took the risk of paying one of the traffickers who took them to Libya in the back of a truck. The journey lasted six days. Amid stories of refugees being dumped in the desert, left to die, they considered their chances of reaching their destination alive to be fairly low.

To their relief and amazement, they arrived safely in Libya where, like cattle, they were transported across the country in a lorry to the coast. Some of their fellow travellers died en route and at every checkpoint or changeover they prepared themselves either to be discovered or kidnapped. After a treacherous eighteen hour boat journey which had claimed many lives before them, they landed in Italy. Michael knew that Italy wasn't granting asylum to many Eritreans so, despite the sheer exhaustion of weeks of gruelling travel and two years on the run, they continued their journey to Britain. The neighbour had looked after Michael all along the way. In return, Michael, who'd given money to his brother when he was in hiding in Eritrea, had enough wired over to pay for the last leg of the journey for them both.

Earlier this year, they finally arrived safely in Surrey, in the back of a lorry transporting vegetables. Naturally, Michael said that God had looked after them every step of the perilous journey. When you listen to the tale, it's nothing less than a miracle that they made it in the end. Sadly, the dispersal system meant that Michael's neighbour (whose name I don't know) was sent to Liverpool, but they have since been in touch through the refugee centres' network, which is excellent. What an amazing man. Amazing? Any words I choose to describe the horror and enormity of what he has been through and the respect I have for him, appear weak and trivial on the page; they don't do him justice. Nothing I write can be a fitting tribute to this man's bravery and commitment to his faith.

I am going to sleep counting my blessings.

Tuesday 24 September

Spent a quiet time at home, alone. Lucas has been helping some new clients at the Centre and advising them on their claims — two men from Afghanistan, fleeing from the Taliban. Their English is good but they have little in the way of documents to support their identity. They are in for a long haul. Didn't see him but it feels good that he's around. Plenty of time to be together later. Ooh — not sure if that was a lurch or a butterfly down there!

Thursday 26 September

Wham bam, thank you mammogram. Another essential evil. I'd completely forgotten about my appointment! Although I am well aware of the date now that I keep a diary, I use a weekly calendar for appointments. With so much for my brain to cope with recently, I hadn't turned the page for this week. There it was: Mammogram 11.30 a.m. Thursday September 26th! It was sheer luck that I wasn't having a lie-in and that Lucas wasn't here to distract me from such trivialities as turning over the calendar.

Before undergoing my first experience of the mammogram van — sounds vaguely like a Marc Bolan B-side — I imagined some contactless x-ray contraption. Why? I have no idea but that idyllic breast-friendly scenario couldn't be further from the truth. I am eternally grateful to the NHS for this service and am well aware of its life-saving properties, but a mammogram, like spa days and childbirth, is a well-kept secret belonging on the dark side of womankind. Yet again, no one had enlightened me as to what happens inside the mammogram van. For a start, being located in your local supermarket car park, your brain tells you 'it's like going shopping,' where nothing particularly dreadful happens to you apart from discovering that they're out of the cheap brand of chopped tomatoes or choosing the wrong queue with the lovely and well-intentioned till operator who chats after every swipe. Or, as would frequently happen in the past, bumping into a parent when all that's rattling round in your trolley is a litre bottle of vodka, tonic, wine and five ready meals.

No, like healthcare professionals everywhere, the mammogram vanners (aka radiographers) are always kind (on the outside) welcoming (there's no escape) and business-like (there to do a job). Suddenly, when you're least expecting it, your boobs are squashed almost flat in a vice-like contraption, like two water-filled balloons being stood on by a circus elephant. Cruelty on three counts: to elephants, balloons, and you. Then, the second you think they're about to pop, the torture ends. Phew! Yes, I know it's for my own good health and wellbeing, and I promise I'm not denying the wonders of science or the wonderful health service. Today's experience was slightly better because I knew that the vice would stop crushing before they popped, unlike the first time when there was no guarantee.

Then, you have that awful period of uncertainty waiting for the results. All part of God's punishment for us getting older. Please make it be negative. I have been through enough this year and have my new life to cope with. I don't think I can take any more.

Friday 27 September

Centre was lively. Luckily Lucas didn't call in — I feel such a fraud when I'm there, pretending I barely know him. It's a strain. No, I am not looking for sympathy. I can hear you very clearly pointing out that it's all my own fault. I am constantly worrying about the mammogram results.

Sunday 29 September

A flurry of activity to take my mind off the mammogram. My life has gone from having very little to occupy my mind and body, to having far too much to do — I can't win! Lucas is going down to London next week to stay with his friends in Southwark who he met through the lawyers, to suss out some work opportunities. He's very excited about it. Readers, those of you who never knew Lucas may think him a chancer, taking advantage of me and my situation, but that is not the case at all! He was mortified when I told him I'd have to put up the deposit for a rented place, or it would take over a year for him to save up to pay half each on the income from a few Spanish and salsa classes. 'Your daughter will think I'm a terrible man,' he said. I assured him she didn't and that she fully understood, although I wouldn't put the odd cynical, protective comment past some of my friends. After all, it's early days by anyone's standards to be moving in with a man you've known for a matter of months.

October

Tuesday 1 October

October already! Time is marching on so started by clearing out my junk, room by room. It's a mammoth task which needed doing, so it's spurred me into action. Not sure if enlisting Simon's help will make the job easier, or ten times more difficult by arguing about everything he will try and force me to bin! He's a minimalist when it comes to furnishing and accessories! Can't believe I'll be leaving my house that I love so dearly. Some people retire to Spain, France or to the coast. I'm retiring to London or rather, *semi*-retiring because I will have to, and want to, work. It will be a way of meeting people. It's almost as if it's not happening to me. Like a fuzzy dream. Feeling surprisingly calm about it today.

Friday 4 October

I'm often too shattered these days to be bothered to write the diary but I know it's good to keep busy, having suffered the consequences of having too little to do.

Did my duty of an hour's decluttering then went to the Centre. Afterwards, took Minika for a coffee — to confess! At the very least, I owe it to her to let her know that I'm leaving. She's been such a good friend. She thinks it's extremely exciting and romantic. Poor, lovely, kind Minika, still waiting for her Leave to Remain status. I wish something exciting or romantic would happen to her. I know she feels rather special to be part of the secret — which is great for her, but makes me feel even more guilt-ridden when I'm at the Centre. 'I have told you Lizzie, there are good rules and bad rules. Two people are very happy now.' She's right, though I'm not sure I'd agree if I were an older, male volunteer with a younger female client. What a hypocrite I am! I've told Lucas to steer well clear of the Centre when I'm there, to be on the safe side. He has his phone now so life is a whole lot easier. I'm tempted to ring him all the time but I want to remain cool, not look clingy and, more importantly, he could be at the Centre and someone might notice 'Lizzie' flashing up on the screen. Might ask him to change it to 'L' or something equally as cryptic.

Tuesday 8 October

Feeling ready to tackle the garden in preparation for renting out the house — two daunting prospects in one sentence — I decided a trip to the garden centre was in order. MISTAKE! If anything was going to dampen my ardour, then the garden centre certainly did the job.

BEWARE: a garden centre is a trap! It is a misnomer — not a garden centre at all but a cleverly disguised shopping centre. In fact, the gardening part is an incidental extra. Lured inside by the promise of sprucing up your herbaceous borders and enhancing your bushy areas, there is no escape until you have been exposed to almost everything and anything that has ever been produced for the household consumer. You think I'm exaggerating? Okay, how about a pineapple slicer? Who, in their right mind needs one of those? Use a bloody knife! Do NOT purchase a gadget you will need twice in your lifetime which will then languish in the back of your drawer till it's put out to grass at the charity shop. Here's another one: a whole section on 'travel fragrance'! I ask you? We call them 'air fresheners' and so should they. The rules surrounding car air fresheners are simple: they should be shaped like a fir tree and smell of pine. NOT 'fruits of the forest' emanating from a teddy bear! What has a teddy got to do with fruits of the forest? Not even a real bear so that the item could be used to disguise the smell of excrement that it had left in the woods.

It said 'forest' and it was a teddy not a grizzly bear, ridiculous. Mingling with all manner of scented candles, the place stank to high heaven.

Moving on past the deli selling food ranging from expensive to extortionate; everything from quails' eggs to home smoked duck breast — YUK! Then soft play, toy section, kitchenware (including hi-vis utensils). Do you cook in a dangerous, dark area? To my left, comfortable yet unsightly shoes, an array of highly unfashionable woollen clothing then, as I was swinging by the driving gloves, it dawned on me: everything in there was geared towards the over fifty-fives; retired people taking their grandchildren out for the day. I looked around me and, sure enough, as it wasn't a weekend, I was the youngest person in there, not counting the under fours. That is a definite plus of the garden centre, but I didn't want to be included in their demographic at all. You can't have it all ways I suppose. Grandparents galore, mooching around the tropical fish tanks and through to pet accessories where you will find every size and colour of animal harness imaginable. When I was a child it was considered positively avant-garde to have a red leash for your dog. After all, a dog leash was a functional piece of leather — black or brown. Now it appears that a pet is a consumer, with its owner hanging around garden centres in the desperate hope of accessorising it with the latest in furry fashion. Eventually I managed to find the escape route and paid for the few pansies I had trailed around the place, having almost forgotten what I had come in for, and was asked if I wanted to join their club. Not bloody likely, thank you. Then, when I was safely through the automatic doors and released back into society, up pops the ubiquitous double glazing salesperson — oh yes I forgot to buy the double glazing when I was at the supermarket earlier so I'd better have some. Again, I politely declined — they are simply doing their job after all.

I drove home feeling shell-shocked and depressed at the stark realisation that I am now the target market of the present day garden centre. First Autumn Silvers — now them. They are all after my silver pound.

Unceremoniously, I dumped the pansies, still trapped in their containers and suffocating in carrier bags, on the patio to be dealt with at another time — if I can ever BA.

Wednesday 9 October

More avoidance tactics today: drove to the supermarket instead of gardening and decluttering. I still appreciate the joy of driving alone, having suffered years of bad-tempered Twat insisting on driving yet always being one brake away from road rage. Being driven everywhere by a man infuriated me, but I couldn't be bothered to argue. Of course I was encouraged to drive when it suited him, if there was drinking involved, for example, but even then he'd manage to enrage me by committing the offence of 'helping' me to drive: saying 'Stop,' when the traffic lights changed to amber, and 'Go,' when they were on green. Inevitably I'd yell, 'There's nothing wrong with my eyesight you know!' but the very worst sin he committed on a regular basis was thanking the other drivers on my behalf. Grr … I can feel my blood coming to the boil, better simmer down. Again, more shouting would ensue as I protested about his interference 'WILL YOU STOP DOING THAT! I WAS ABOUT TO THANK THEM! HOW WOULD YOU LIKE IT IF….' and so it would go on and on and on. If he'd been drinking he'd shout back and the entire journey would be a nightmare. I'm so happy those days are behind me.

It got me thinking about what exactly constitutes *the right amount of thanking* when driving. I like to think I'm a super-courteous road user who always acknowledges considerate behaviour from others. However, *over*-thanking is not cool. Lorry drivers perform exactly the right amount of thanking, often with slight nod of the head, perfectly fulfilling the purpose. I have devised a code which I adhere to rigidly:

- driver stops to let you past — whole hand plus arm raised off steering wheel, headlights flashed — an optional extra
- driver stops to give way at a 'Give Way to Oncoming Vehicles' sign — index finger raised, hand remains on steering wheel (minimal thanks — they were supposed to stop)
- driver thanks you for stopping to let them past — four fingers raised, hand remains on steering wheel (if lorry driver — nod of head to acknowledge the thanks)

One phase of my life I'm not looking forward to is the point at which the car begins to drive *you*. No, it's not a form of robotics, it occurs naturally when you are on the cusp of giving up your licence: you are concentrating so hard on the mechanics of driving, usually dangerously slowly, manoeuvring the beast around corners and straightening it up again, that the vehicle appears entirely out of control.

At this stage of your motoring life, you are a member of the group least likely to engage in any amount of thanking whatsoever.

Friday 11 October

Woke up at twenty past three this morning in a cold sweat, wondering if I was doing the right thing! Decided to read to distract myself. Then had a weird flashback to Twat days, remembering how he'd moan about my reading light in bed, stopping him from sleeping for five minutes before he started to snore the roof down so that I couldn't sleep a wink for the entire night. I'm now remembering clearly how bad it really was, as opposed to the rose-tinted version of events with the crap carefully and cleverly filtered out. I can't imagine Lucas behaving like that and, if he did, I certainly wouldn't put up with it. I feel one thousand percent better than I did last year, about everything. Incidentally, Simon Cowell, anything more than one hundred percent is mathematically impossible, but it comes in handy on occasions, I'll grant you that.

Survived my day at the Centre by the skin of my teeth. Kept a low profile. Had a lovely email from Lucas, asking me again if I'd changed my mind having had even more time to think about it! Told him not to be silly. It still feels odd, thinking about moving away and into a serious relationship, I can't deny it. I kept that last thought to myself, however.

Feeling drained after the broken sleep last night and all the excitement — or is it stress? I've never been sure where to draw the line on that one.

Monday 14 October

Shit — I have been called back for another mammogram. Tomorrow! They're not hanging around — does that mean it looks particularly bad? Not telling Lucas, or anyone else for that matter, until afterwards.

During topsy-turvy events of the past few weeks, I stopped obsessing about the mammogram results. Now I'm terrified about the possibility of having breast cancer. I've read the statistics so I shouldn't be worried — but that's easier said than done. I know survivors of breast cancer. I know people undergoing treatment for it. Their bravery and stoicism never ceases to amaze me. I can't imagine behaving as they do. Friends who, having lost their hair during chemotherapy, wear a wig and joke about it. Some even try new colours or styles, others, understandably, choose to stay close to their own natural, familiar hair. Then there are the equally admirable group of friends who choose not to wear a wig. Instead, they wear a hat, a cap, a headscarf, sometimes nothing. I am not that brave. If I get to that stage I will become even more of a recluse, as Sam keeps calling me. I will hide my head through cowardice, vanity and self-pity.

What did I do in a previous life that was so bad? Did I steal a sheep or refuse to kiss the bishop's ring? I need to calm down. Please God, in case you exist, forgive me for shunning you in the past, please make me a statistical norm and allow me not to have cancer, if only for now. You can delay it if you want, God, but now I am not strong enough to face it. I am not like those beautiful, glorious, courageous women sporting wigs, caps, bald heads or turbans. I am me. I am weak, useless. I am sorry.

3.00 a.m. Brandy needed. Not good.

Tuesday 15 October

I was shaking before I went into the clinic. Had to employ serious calming tactics and deep breathing. Gripped with fear and panic. Feelings were similar to being on the London Eye, except at ground level. Then had to go up the escalator. It started again, felt dizzy. How stupid! Went in and found everyone looking terrified, all having been recalled. The nurses were again marvellous. So well trained and highly skilled at dealing with nervous patients i.e. everyone there. They go out of their way to make you feel at ease. I was trembling when I went in. Luckily, mine was another mammogram. Some had to have a biopsy, depending upon what had been detected by the first one. I had it without resenting the pain this time. I was prepared to withstand anything if it helped to prevent the remotest possibility of having breast cancer. I know that's not a logical thought process but that's how I felt, devoid of rational thinking.

An agonising fifteen minutes later — ungrateful, I know, because some people wait two weeks for the result of a biopsy, but when you're in there you become entirely self-obsessed and the fifteen minutes feels like an hour as irrational-brain kick-starts yet again with thoughts like, 'If it was clear they'd see instantly and be back within a minute, so that means there's definitely a problem,' and other such nonsense.

It was clear. All fine. I nearly said, 'What? It can't be!' Rushed off before they could change their minds. I know it's not a subjective opinion, it's a medical fact, but irrational-brain wasn't taking any chances and I almost skipped out of there. I felt like a child, and promised never to be stupid again, drink alcohol or harm my body in any way — which will last all of two or three days I suspect. I am grateful for my health. My mind isn't quite so sound, but at least my body is rallying round and holding up under the pressure — or some of it, that is. Relief. My thoughts are with the woman who was still in the waiting room when I left, kept back for further investigation. Alone, with fear written all over her face, poor love. She was much younger than I am. Nature is cruel, very cruel.

Weds 16 October — old habits of laziness.

A day off from the tidying, binning, and filling the garage with bags for the charity shop. I was exhausted after yesterday and spent a long time talking to Lucas about it, trying to explain why I didn't want to share it with him, which was hard. He was so sweet and said he felt terribly sorry for me going by myself when he could have come with me. I had the whole rigmarole to go through again after Sam finished work. She was furious with me and said I was never to do that again! Bless her.

Neither of them understands that I didn't want the unnecessary fuss. There would have been plenty of opportunity for sympathy had I been kept back for further tests. I wanted to go it alone, if truth be told. I now realise that wanting to go on my own is a good sign, a sign of recovery, and my strength returning. Every cloud... although in hindsight I could have done with the moral support from someone to save me from my mad brain.

Yes, if there is a next time, I think I will share it with one of them.

Saturday 19 October

Not been doing much, other than thinking a lot and having a quiet time after the mammogram recall.

Sunday 20 October

Sara texted, wanting to meet:
'OMG the web has unravelled...thanks to Chatty Bob. You free?'

She was referring to the ménage a trois situation which I, the older (but not much wiser as it turns out) friend, had sagely warned, 'Oh what a tangled web we weave when first we practise to deceive.' Intrigued, I quickly arranged to see her in town. Do you remember, readers, the Tom and Chris scenario — Tom from the Collingwood pub frequented by Chatty Bob — Sara seeing both at once? It's been going on since Easter but she rarely mentions it in order to avoid the inevitable flack it attracts for playing with fire!

She was clearly upset but already resigned to it and, between cringes, laughing at the audacity of it all! As bad luck would have it, she'd had to employ the decorating services of Chatty Bob for longer than expected. Mindful of the precariousness of the situation, she tried to avoid either of her beaux being there when Bob was around. Apparently, she'd come back on Tuesday with Chris plus fish and chips, expecting Bob to be long gone for early doors at the pub, but there he was, packing up his gear. Sara spent the next ten excruciating minutes gabbling non-stop to prevent Bob calling him 'Tom' or putting his foot right in it e.g. 'Did yous two enjoy the film the other neet?' having seen Sara with Tom in the pub after the Amy Winehouse film at the weekend. To make matters worse, Tom and Chris look fairly similar and to a drunken man they would appear identical. After what felt like an hour, Chatty Bob finally exited with a cheeky, 'Have ye been drinking already?' quip to the now jabbering Sara. Relieved to see that Chris thought nothing of it, largely due to the fact that Sara can talk for England, she assumed she was in the clear.

Three days later, it transpires, she and Tom were in the pub after a meal in town, when Bob walked up to them 'mortal drunk' as Sara described him, and asked if they'd enjoyed the fish and chips. Tom told him they'd been for a Chinese meal and before Sara could answer Bob said, 'Naa man, the other neet, at Sara's, Tuesday it was, aye Tuesday.' Then the penny dropped, 'Ah naa, it wasn't ye was it?' As the voice trailed off, so did he. Tom had merely stared at Sara, whose red face gave it all away: embarrassed, caught out, game over. She'd told Tom at the weekend that she couldn't see him until Friday because she, Saint Sara, was helping her granny with her shopping! Unable or unwilling to think up any more lies, she said nothing and waited for the onslaught. But none came. Poor Tom looked crushed, turned, and left the pub. She hasn't heard from him since. The incorrigible Sara, however, was so upset, not sorry to have two-timed the poor lad, but because she fancies him more than Chris and was now left with the inferior one! Oh the remorselessness of being thirtysomething! 'Howay then Auntie Lizzie,' she mocked, 'Say, 'I told you so',' Instead, I put on the most serious tone of voice I could muster and said, 'Well, Sara. If you've learned one thing from this sorry mess, it's that you must never, *ever* rely on Chatty Bob to keep his big mouth shut!' That cheered her up.

It made a welcome change from obsessing about my own future and I had a great laugh too — always good for the soul.

Monday 21 October

Students

In recovery after a disastrously timed trip to the local supermarket — one of those mini-me versions of a proper grown-up one and I am about to explode! Dubbed by my friends as 'the worst shop in the world', the place comes with its own set of rules:

Do NOT attempt to enter the shop between the hours of five and seven p.m. on a Monday: students all shopping, having been away or on a liquid diet all weekend.

Do NOT attempt to enter the shop between the hours of five and seven p.m. on a Friday night: students all shopping for said liquid diet.

Serves me right for breaking rule number one.

Students around here are an alien breed compared to my own university peers. The worst shop in the world attracts a disproportionate number of ex-public school students — the 'Hoorahs'. They shop in packs, blocking the unfeasibly narrow aisles with blonde hair, expensive suede boots (females) and floppy quiffs (males). Lots of 'Yah'-ing can be heard as they select sharing platters of overpriced meats, packs of olives floating in gunk that makes them, gram for gram, as expensive as gold. Trendy flavoured vodka and designer label gin — never the shop's own brand — Pimms and, very often, champagne. I think I was thirty before I tasted real champagne, but here they can be observed popping it into the basket like it's a litre of milk. Then they take the enormous basket, now laden with goods, to the shortest of the three evil queues that you had previously identified and beat you to the end of it. Self- service is always the longest and most troublesome, with the machine moaning at you all the time. What the hell do you expect me to do with the item if I can't put it in the bloody bagging area? What do mean, 'Unexpected item in the bagging area?' What exactly *were* you expecting in there, a python, an aardvark, a natterjack toad? You then find yourself inevitably behind the three students with fewer than ten items, although the sign incorrectly says 'less than'. Items are countable nouns … don't get me started. I can hear Sam sighing heavily, 'Whatever,' in an exasperated manner as I write this!

So — while you are smugly congratulating yourself on your wise choice of checkout, they split the eight items into three groups to pay for them separately, with cards that are tucked firmly away in their purses at the bottom of their real (not fake) oversized designer handbags. Aaaaargghh! Deep breaths must be taken at this point when you sense the blood pressure sky rocketing and your heart palpitating. After employing meditation techniques, imagining yourself in another place, a calm place, a place that you love (not loathe), you are finally served and assume that the end is in sight. WRONG! Where is the worst place for large groups of egocentric students to stand and catch up on the weekend's antics? Correct — the shop doorway! The whole length and breadth of it blocked, and with more, excitable ones barging their way past them to enter the shop, a human logjam is created, preventing any exit at all, let alone a sharp one.

One evening last year, after a very stressful day with a staff meeting thrown in, I yelled, ''SCUSE ME!' at the top of my voice. Although it had the desired effect, I left, feeling like a mad, ranting old woman, my target audience plus the entire top end of the shop staring at me, aghast! Naturally, when I (aka Moses) parted the sea of people and exited the hateful shop, the ripples of laughter reached my ears as I rushed to my car thinking 'deeper breaths next time'. I didn't return for a long while, half expecting to see my face on a poster, like the pubwatch scheme operating in some of the less salubrious establishments, showing who is barred. 'Worstshopintheworldwatch'?

I know I'm supposed to be calmer these days but that shop would test the patience of a saint, and I ain't one of *them*, that's a well-established fact!

Tuesday 22 October

I know I ought to be clearing, tidying and rendering the place spotless, but:
CBA.

Far too interested in distracting myself with the diaries which I don't expect to be accompanying me to London due to acute lack of space.

Feeling like a recalcitrant child, I ignored the mess and reached into the diary box for a lucky dip.
Census Man
This event took place in my late twenties, pre-Twat. Happened upon one of my most shameful tales of over-indulgence ever! This story I have retold on many occasions as:

a) a funny anecdote
b) a cautionary tale about pacing oneself where alcohol is concerned, particularly when a long-haul session is on the cards e.g. wedding or similar

Take heed, younger readers, or you may be in danger of choking on your own vomit, which is never attractive.

By all accounts (mainly other people's!) I had a fantastic time at my lovely friend Maria's wedding. Although I was more than old enough to know better, I got carried away with the excitement of it all and drank so much that, had it been water, it would certainly have accommodated at least a thousand tropical fish. Not content with a whole afternoon of merriment, we continued at a hotel and played silly games involving more alcohol. Eventually, I was bundled into a taxi and dispatched home, unable to string a sentence together and can remember the next scene as if it were yesterday, no diary required. I opened the taxi door and literally fell out of it, in a drunken heap on the pavement, exactly like Patsy or Eddie in *Absolutely Fabulous*! The poor taxi driver had to help me to the door where I insisted I was fine. I awoke the next morning in a heap in the hallway, my face pressed against the skirting board behind the front door. I was still wearing wedding-disco sparkly clothing, but the shine had been taken off the outfit by the vomit which started in my hair and continued down the front of my top, petering out to a thin trickle at my waistband! Cue the cries of, 'You could have died, choking on your own vomit!' and similar reprimands.

As I was about to attempt to crawl up to the shower, the doorbell rang and for some absurd reason I answered it. There stood a poor, unsuspecting young man, who politely said, 'Sorry to get you up,' like it was completely normal to go to bed in full disco gear, accessorised with vomit, then, 'Here's your census form.' After realising I was in a state of utter bewilderment and noting that Sunday morning was not such a good time for the government to distribute census forms after all, he contemplated the best course of action and muttered, 'I'll put it through the letter box, shall I?' Like a zombie, I nodded and closed the door, noticing that the house alarm was flashing which meant I must have set it off when I came in then crashed out before I had the chance to turn it off! For all I knew, the neighbours may have come running but were unable to raise the living dead from the comfort of her hallway floor. Oh the humiliation of it all! I had to hide from them for weeks afterwards. Showered, slept for a few hours then called upon the services of Debs who came round to pack for me as we were going away on holiday early the next day. I lay there, like some sickly dauphin princess, pointing and nodding, directing her to various drawers and cupboards to select holiday essentials. Bless her!

The diary entry was so much more detailed than my blurred memory of events. I did laugh, despite the shame, and was terrified of alcohol for a long time afterwards. Wasn't sure who 'JM' was but I had snogged the poor guy at some point during the festivities which was, apparently, a good thing. Remember: never write in code!

Friday 25 October

I glanced at the garden, not having done anything at all about tidying it up since Garden Centre Hell and caught sight of the pansies — all dead! I'd completely forgotten about them and should have realised, being a primary school teacher for all those years, that they would die after a few days without water, squashed into a plastic bag with no light. I am *not* going back there to replace them. You can't make me, please! Aaagh no!

Consumed with guilt, I sorted out a drawer packed with things of absolutely no use whatsoever, by way of a punishment.

Saturday 26 October

Lucas called round this afternoon, unexpectedly, which is always a nerve-racking event. I whisked him inside, out of sight from the general public, and assured him that I had been tidying up and clearing things out, even though it doesn't appear to be the case quite yet. Not sure if he believed me! We had some tea then snuggled up listening to music and before we knew it, it was eleven o'clock so he stayed over — luscious!

Tuesday 29 October

'I want to go trick-or-treating on Thursday.'
'You can't. You're a forty-five year old man!'
Lucas has always loved the American-imported Halloween craziness. They have it in Colombia too. I once went to New York around Halloween and almost every house was decorated — it was madness! When I was teaching, I loved creating witchy and skeleton dances with the kids. Spooky poems, making hats, masks, and writing ghost stories. It was a fantastic stimulus and excellent fun. One of my funniest school stories occurred on a teaching practice shortly before Halloween, with a class of eight and nine-year-olds in Whitley Bay. It remains one of the wittiest retorts I've ever heard from a child so young. I'd been demonstrating how to make an extra-scary Halloween mask and, when I'd finished, put it on. I then removed the mask and was about to issue the next instruction, when a voice piped up from the back, 'Take it off!' I had to say, 'Oh yes, very funny,' as if it wasn't, but to this day I think of that little heckle every time I see a Halloween mask.

Wednesday 30 October

Still CBA with the house clearing.
Agreed that Lucas could come round tomorrow for Halloween and we'd host trick-or-treating as every year some of the neighbourhood kids call at the house, along with some random chancers who obviously aren't local and come in the hope of getting a few free sweets. And why

not? I don't think there are any hard and fast rules attached to trick-or-treat.

November

Friday 1 November

A hilarious night! I felt and acted like a teenager again, being extraordinarily silly. Finally agreed to buy two masks (cue teaching practice heckle) stocked up with sweets for trick-or-treaters, and reluctantly hollowed out a pumpkin — as if a child had made it — to display on the doorstep. The first group arrived, dressed in beautiful, lovingly hand-made costumes with their responsible, concerned parents standing at the end of the path on paedophile-watch. Sweets were despatched and they went on their merry way, much to Lucas's delight. Another group came as we were about to eat, but we did our duty and sent them away happy.

Soon afterwards, there was a knock at the neighbours' door and we peeped out of the curtains to see who would be coming to us next. There was a group of much older kids, no parents in tow, who had made zero effort on the costumes front and were obviously in it not for fun, but for what they could profit from the evening. The neighbours were out so the disgruntled kids scattered what looked like flour over the garden path, leaving a horrible mess. On seeing this, Lucas said, 'Time for the masks.' His was hideous: a grotesque werewolf mask and he popped on a pair of my furry gloves to complete the look. My witchy mask was equally revolting and I humoured him further by donning a black velvet cloak I'd kept from the seventies! The impact was greater than I could have imagined: we opened the door and Lucas let out a blood curdling 'RAAGH', sending the screaming, swearing kids charging down the path, accidentally dropping their bag of flour, safely contained within its carrier bag! I laughed so hard I couldn't stand up and unintentionally cackled like a witch, adding to the horror of it all for the poor, unsuspecting teenagers. We knew that by the time they got home they'd be laughing about it and would have a great tale to tell at school the next day. Either that or their parents would call the police...

Now I have two Halloween mask stories; not many people can rival that.

Saturday 2 November

HELL'S BELLS — I sound like my mum — IT'S ALL KICKING OFF HERE! Hilary is leaving Miserable Jeff! Don't know what to make of it all. Apparently, she's been inspired by my happiness and drastic decision to move to London, which may be flattering but I now feel responsible for the situation. What if she's miserable without Miserable Jeff? And there's no doubt at all that he will be Even More Miserable Jeff without her. Shit, the pressure! Nonetheless, I am proud of my lovely, loyal and brave friend. Good on her. She called this morning, tearfully asking to meet up.

Hilary drove over, stayed for around three hours then left. Poor soul. Never regarded her as the single type, but here's a whole new chapter for her, too. Usual story of being unhappy (even more so than Twat and I) for years but stayed together because of the kids. Now that the youngest is away at university, there's no point in pretending any more. Jeff? More furious than upset, she tells me — though I suspect he'll be covering it up. Men and women are so different, especially the Jeff types — older generation, pre-feminism, scared or unwilling to show their feelings, with the result that the woman has absolutely no doubt she's doing the right thing. Too proud to beg, ask her to reconsider or give it another try. Instead he'd stomped off and has refused to speak to her ever since — that was three days ago.

Hilary said, 'I feel like an enormous boulder has been lifted off my back, returning me to the wild. I can breathe again.' She must have been formulating that one for the last three days! It sounds like she's done the right thing. Just as she'd quizzed me on the practicalities when I told her about my move, I reciprocated by asking what her plans were. 'Easy,' she asserted, 'rent a flat in town while the house is up for sale. Don't want to be stuck out there for an eternity, I want to live a little!' Luckily, money isn't an issue in Hilaryworld. Incredible! Don't know what's happened to my cautious, family-orientated-verging-on-obsessive friend, but I'm loving the replacement!

She refused the offer of a room on the grounds that Jeff would think she had 'taken up with another man' as he'd said, accusingly. She didn't want him to have the satisfaction of blaming anyone other than himself for the split. I asked if she'd tried talking to him before, in case he had been blissfully unaware of her unhappiness. She said she had talked to him several times over the years, telling him exactly what he could do to salvage the relationship, but he made absolutely no attempt to alter his ways! I'm now satisfied that Miserable Jeff has been given sufficient chances in the past and CBA to change a thing.

So, that's why Hilary always spoke (non-stop) about her perfect relationship, her life and family. It was a façade, to cover up her grim and loveless situation. Let's face it, if you start moaning about your life partner and let slip how desperately unhappy you are, your friends will think you weak and stupid for staying put. At least that's how many of us think, so we pretend; we live a lie. She's going to see a lawyer tomorrow and call a few estate agents afterwards. Wow — she doesn't let the grass grow! What a turn-up for the books. I'm excited for her! Shame I won't be around for long to be a part of her new-found freedom; sounds like it could be fun.

Sunday 3 November

I need to divert my mind from thinking about Lucas going to London this week and maybe having too much of a good time with his new friends. There, I've said it. I sound like a mean, bitter, possessive creature. He's going to look for work, for God's sake. What's the matter with me? I'm a tad fragile today, that's all. Delved into the diary box, my sanctuary. Knew roughly where to look: first year of college.

I'd spent an evening at my mum and dad's house in floods of tears because I'd finished with Mark, my boyfriend of two years. I'd snogged Sandy, someone I'd had my roving eye on for a while, at the Students' Union sixties disco. The feeling of guilt and wretchedness is almost tangible as I can remember wailing, 'I wish it was the other way round!' Naturally, at that tender age, I wasn't aware that it is in fact far, far better to be the chuck*er,* rather than the chuck*ee.* I remember becoming more used to it after that first time — even after a few pages there was no further mention of poor Mark; it was all 'Sandy, Sandy, Sandy'! It did make me chuckle at how fickle we were then.

Hope Hilary moves on as quickly as that. Somehow I'm not so sure.

Monday 4 November

Had a great discussion with Lucas about the origins of Bonfire Night and he had plenty of stories of similar festivals in Colombia. They love a bit of pyrotechnics over there! It goes with their passionate nature and their joie de vivre. Dying to take him to the free fireworks display organised by the council. People joke about their council tax going up in smoke, but everyone loves it.

Wednesday 6 November

Fireworks!
Lucas came round for tea last night. I always have a furtive scan around when he comes to the house, in case anyone from the Centre happens to be passing, checking for any professional misconduct that could be occurring. He always makes a joke, 'Quick, quick, before they arrest you!' Then I drag him in, chastise him for being facetious, and hug him tightly so I can feel those wiry arms around me. It's now a ritual.

Ate traditional Bonfire Night food: sausages, baked potatoes and baked beans then joined the crowds heading for the Stadium — a playing field in Sandyford. Hundreds and hundreds go: students, families, couples, friends, people from all sections of the community, apart from the elderly who don't tend to venture out at night in the winter. The atmosphere is fantastic with the appreciative crowd punctuating the fireworks with 'Ooh' and 'Aaah'. Too many people record the whole event on their phone. I always maintain that if you record it through a screen, then watch it back, perhaps on another screen, you will never see it in its full splendour. You will miss its explosive grandiosity, the true shapes and colours though you'll think you witnessed it all. I pity them, but they are the techno generation and they will not change.

Towards the end of the display everyone wonders if they have seen the final firework, until a new batch shoots into the sky to squeals of delight from the crowd. Lasting almost half an hour, the council has yet again done us proud and we set off for the Free Trade pub to catch a glimpse of more fireworks along the river banks, stretching for miles. I told Lucas about the year that a guy marched into the pub garden with a terrier and six industrial sized rockets slung over his shoulder, appropriated from somewhere. It was brilliant! The dog didn't bat an eyelid during the whole extremely noisy proceedings. Sadly, the gear must have been under lock and key this year as he didn't show up.

Lucas stayed over: more fireworks. Sorry, I couldn't resist that rather obvious one! Thinking back to the display, he was like a small child from beginning to end, joining in with the oohs and aaahs, his face lit up, animated like a sparkler. He looked beautiful, happy, and relaxed. That moment will stay with me for ever. He, on the other hand, may not.

Saturday 9 November

Spent the past few days with Hilary, Sam and Sara. Lucas got the coach down to London yesterday and I'm missing him, although I've been super-busy. It's been a whirlwind of sorting, tidying and numerous trips to the Centre and charity shops with clothing, kitchen items and other 'stuff' or 'shite' as Sam calls it. When I say 'charity shops' I don't mean *that* one! I have to walk around the block to avoid passing *that* one and must have clocked up hundreds of extra avoidance miles as a punishment for being outspoken! Bags and bags, boxes and yet more boxes. It feels good to have less clutter in my life, although I must admit it was hard to let go of some of it. After all, it's like letting go of your past life, which I know is supposed to be cathartic, but can verge on traumatic at the same time...

It's been hard. I permanently lurch between acute excitement and sheer terror with a permanent undercurrent of self-doubt. Sam's been so supportive — I know she's proud of her adventurous, go-getting mother, which is lovely, but beneath the surface I see the way she looks at me, with worry in her beautiful green eyes — from *my* side of the family, of course.

Hilary — she's something else! It's now her turn for the aliens to invade her body — either aliens or drug-pushers, she's as high as a kite! Overexcited about her new flat she annoyingly refers to as 'the apartment' simply because it's near the Quayside. It's a flat, Hilary — get used to it! She wants me to come shopping with her for soft furnishings. What? I don't have the time or, quite frankly, the inclination. Spiteful I admit, but it will rub my nose in it as I look forward to living in some miniscule studio apartment, or bedsit as it ought to be called. But I have Lucas and I wouldn't want to swap him for a few coordinating cushions. She's joined a gym near the flat already — and signed up for salsa dancing and Zumba classes elsewhere. Impressive! She hasn't moved in yet. I think they're diversion tactics to stop her dwelling on what Jeff's going to do. Her son and two daughters, like mine, are being very protective over her, bemused by it all.

Sunday 10 November

Feeling slightly stressed, if I'm honest, but I'd choose stress over depression any day. At least I feel *something* instead of *nothing*. I know I'm stressed because I've started talking to myself in public — again. When I was going through a bad patch at work, I would find myself tearing around the worst shop in the world saying, 'Pickle,' or 'Bananas,' and other items from the list. Yesterday I caught myself in the same shop saying, 'Condoms,' loudly this time! Not that condoms were on the list, it was Worcester Sauce but in my head I was thinking condiments/condoms and it slipped out of my mouth, so to speak! I sounded like an eccentric, muttering old woman with the onset of Tourette's syndrome. Many of the adjectives in that sentence are apt; I shall leave you to choose which they are. After all, they're used to me in that shop so I might as well revert to type.

However, what I'm experiencing is more like excitement than normal stress — what is *normal* stress? It certainly feels different from work stress but I mustn't put myself under pressure, Christmas is a long way off — though judging by the shops and bombardment of advertising you'd think it was tomorrow. And, it's my birthday soon. How different it'll be to last year, when I was hurtling towards the doldrums without realising it. Instead, I was basking in the luxury of not having to go to work, assuming that a life would come a-cold calling at my door when the novelty wore off, with a range of exciting options of how best to occupy my time. Funnily enough it didn't pan out that way; I was blissfully unaware of what was round the corner.

Tuesday 12 November

Lucas is back — sadly not for long, but I mustn't bring down the mood by being a misery. He's very positive and feels rejuvenated after the months of angst brought about by his asylum claim. One of the guys who the lawyer put him in contact with has a room in Elephant and Castle which will be free from this weekend as a housemate is returning to Ecuador. It's all rather sudden — not surprised he didn't tell me on the phone. We are both old enough to know that some news is best broken face to face. Imagine living in a place called Elephant, with a castle to boot! It's totally bizarre and very, very funny. Lucas can take over his salsa classes three nights a week and while he was there he made contact with a language school advertising for Spanish teachers. He has to show them his qualifications which he had the presence of mind to bring with him when he left Colombia. Some asylum seekers have to leave in such a hurry that they have nothing to prove their identity, let alone their profession. It's a huge relief to have some work organised, not that three salsa classes a week will pay a London rent, but it's a start.

He kept his place at the hostel here otherwise the Centre would want to know where he was living, but will have to give it up at the end of the week. He stayed over. Lovely to have him back, although, over the last few days I've had a taste of a new life without him — and it didn't feel too bad, if I'm honest.

Friday 15 November

Feeling desperately sad. Took Lucas to the bus station this afternoon after the Centre. Made a fool of myself by crying when we said our goodbyes. Trying to stay strong, but I feel like I'm losing him to another life, despite the fact that I'm going to be a part of it. I know that's contradictory but I want him to be a part of my life here. I booked train tickets so he can be back for my birthday weekend. It'll be something to look forward to.

Sunday 17 November

Went to town with Sam and Ben who cheered me up! They're well suited and he clearly worships her which, for a parent, is the main criteria for boyfriend material. It was very sweet of them because they both work full time — he's also in medical physics, at another hospital so time together is precious. Sam insisted I join them, knowing I'd be a bit down after Lucas leaving again so soon.

They were asking about my birthday plans and were adamant about making arrangements there and then. I settled for a meal out with the usual suspects. Lucas will be back for it too. It will be lovely and a welcome break from the never-ending tidying treadmill. I am now through to the next round: cleaning, having completed and survived the decluttering. I must contact the agents. Might do it tomorrow, or Tuesday.

Wednesday 20 November

Another unexpected flurry of excitement over the past few days: Hilary moved into her flat! Rang Monday to ask me for help with the move on Tuesday. Luckily for me, it wasn't the olden days' method of moving where we all helped each other load box after box into a transit van and were treated to beer and takeaway pizza at the end of it. No, no, no; Hilary had packers and bespoke removal women. A great service and no danger of any jokes being cracked about how many boxes of clothes there were. I was there for moral support at her end (fortunately no sign of Miserable Jeff) and to help with the furniture arrangement which involved pointing whilst the women cheerily positioned and moved it several times without rolling their eyes even once. We toasted the new place with wine and a Chinese takeaway. Not a million miles from the old days, after all!

Today I went round with a flat-warming prezzie for her: a beautiful, simple vase she'd admired when we were out once. She was so grateful. I thought she looked very sad, standing alone at the door when I left. I wanted to go back and give her a hug, but she doesn't do sentiment. Think it might be because she's shattered, emotionally drained; I know I am.

Thursday 21 November

Hilary treated me to a meal at Las Estrellas, my favourite Spanish tapas restaurant near the football ground, for helping her with the move. It was fun from beginning to end with Hilary insisting we went back to her new place for more wine — mistake but made perfect sense at the time! Can't believe this is all happening to me. Took a taxi home. Driver attempted to moan about immigration (yawn) so I said, 'Yes, my partner's one of them,' in my teacher's voice. That shut him up.

Friday 22 November

Missing Lucas badly. Playing slushy music, making it worse in one way but better in another. I know he'll be back soon and we'll be living together — stomach lurched again! Can you please, dear Shady Pines readers, let me know by telepathy across the time zones, if this will all be okay because I need to know. I want the stomach-lurching to be because of excitement, not terror.

Starting to find the Centre even more difficult because I am essentially lying to them! Minika, my ally, wasn't there today and Ken was telling me about Lucas going to London to find work! How awkward! Could feel myself blushing like an idiot and then was convinced that he must know something because of the colour of my face. Aaaaagh! It's God's punishment for my unprofessionalism. Everything has its price! Need to book train tickets for London — my recce trip. 'Recce' always looks weird written down. My dad always said it and when I was young we were always 'doing a recce' of somewhere or another! I'm doing a recce of my new life — more lurching. Head's spinning. Brandy beckons. Don't want to go down that rocky road again. These are testing times. Had a lovely, 'Goodnight I miss you Lizzie,' text from Lucas.

Saturday 23 November

Lucas rang this afternoon. Sounded happy and upbeat as he'd picked up another four hours a week of Spanish teaching by calling in at a language school, on the off-chance. It's an adult beginners' group that they are hoping to start in January, so they're delighted with his timing. Some of you will call it 'fate', but you make your own luck and it happens to be the eleventh place he's been to with his CV asking for work. Up until now he was told, 'Sorry, we have all the staff we need.' He must find a few more hours before he's self-sufficient, and that's without my contribution. He's done pretty well through his persistence and determination — it's admirable. After all, no one wants to be saddled with a shirker, however gorgeous they may be!

Talked about dates for the recce. We had a laugh because I'd texted it to him, knowing he'd look up the word immediately, and he said, 'Surely that's an Italian word, like 'focaccia' so it should be pronounced 'rechay' which sounds foul, like you're being sick!' I agreed to ditch my strong principles on spelling and grammar and write 'recky' in the future. We agreed on the first week of December, after my birthday weekend, so we can travel down together. Then realised it's next week — aaagh! I need to get cracking with the house-letting.

Booked train tickets — one step closer. Shudder travels rapidly down spine.

Monday 25 November

Heard the best news ever today — Minika has had her claim approved! At long last she's been granted Leave to Remain! Safety and peace of mind for the next five years, before her case is reviewed again. Naturally, she was euphoric, along with everyone else in the building and we all shed tears. She is a very special, popular person. I had a very selfish thought: I won't be here to see Minika build her new life in Newcastle. She wants to study nursing and I would love to support her through that in any way possible. I felt terribly guilty too, about leaving, swanning off to London. Don't think Minika's life revolves around me, though. I'm probably bigging my part up. I like that phrase.

We had the customary, modest celebration and as soon as I had the chance I rang Lucas, who was thrilled for her. Chose not to tell him about my guilt pangs.

Tuesday 26 November

Yet more cleaning! Yuk, yuk, yuk! Not my pastime of choice, I assure you.

More astonishing news — this is becoming quite a week: Hilary, who is definitely having a mid-life crisis, has been on a dating website and bagged herself a fella! And there was I, feeling sorry for her, worrying about her being all on her ownsome. The little tinker! Talk about reformed character — or something character. 'Reformed' suggests becoming a better person, so I reckon wilder plus more interesting *does* equal 'better', so 'reformed' she is! None of this, 'I'm thinking about going on a dating website,' malarkey, or having to be cajoled and practically press-ganged into it — this woman is taking life by the scruff of the neck and giving it a bloody good shake!

John: a retired teacher — could be burnt out, Hilary, if he's stuck it out till the end — likes eating out (good) and golf (bad) but she's always said she wants to learn how to play golf. It baffles me why anyone would want to, but each to their own. They're a good match on paper. She's not even heeding the advice and having coffee with him — she's going in for the kill and meeting him for a drink! She'll be absolutely fine. I wouldn't fancy my chances in a scrap with Hilary — she's well-built and could floor you with a flick of the wrist. She was a judo and karate expert at school. As we know, there are now all sorts of versions with exotic names, but it's all about fighting in a controlled way and especially handy if you're a woman. She cheered me up immensely, which is the first time in our entire friendship I've said that. A new chapter for all.

Wednesday 27 November

Lunch with Sam. She wanted to discuss my birthday meal, calling it 'The Last Supper' (it runs in the family) which was a bit harsh, then apologised. I have a sinking feeling, a literally heavy heart, when I think of leaving Sam and everyone else. However, something far worse evoked familiar feelings of anger and irritation, similar to those felt in my darkest days also popped up at the lunch table. Something terrible, that has been bugging me for a while but I chose to ignore it — now it's back: alternative serving dishes. Things served on pieces of wood, slate and in all manner of vessels instead of plates: decorative miniature wheelbarrows, tiny crates, and jam jars instead of a glass.

Sam tells me there's a social media group I could join, if I was a social media user of course! Am almost tempted to start so I can join 'We Want Plates'. She says people are quite abusive about the serving ware, such is their passion. Yes, I can see myself joining their ranks. Today, having been served bread for my starter in a flat cap (I kid you not) the main course on a used chopping board (hygiene?) and my dessert in a glass measuring jug, I think I would qualify to join their group. Sam told me she'd eaten fish and chips off a small shovel and a casserole out of a dog bowl — REVOLTING! The very worst one, she thought, was spaghetti bolognese in a pint glass. She doesn't object to it as much as I do but says it's wearing a bit thin. I think it's utter, pretentious twaddle, clearly reaching nonsensical proportions as restaurateurs attempt to outdo each other in the quirkiness stakes, no pun intended! Hmm... thought I was mellowing a little, but it was a mere temporary blip which, I have to admit, is strangely comforting. Will have to ask Sam to help me join a social media website. Sounds like I may have a few allies out there.

After a long, circuitous discussion, we finally decided on a meal at home. At least there won't be the worry of it possibly being served on a rusty old tin lid.

Thursday 28 November

He's back! I have to write the diary when he's not around, though he's under strict instructions not to look in it. That said, I still lock it away. Wasn't born yesterday.

This also entails writing it at all sorts of times because bedtime, the traditional diary-writing slot, is now dedicated to other activities — yes, sex. No use going all 'tut-tut' on me, simply because you, dear readers, may no longer be active in that area. Please recall the days when you were. No, I'm not going to go into details this time, you will have to flick back if you've forgotten them. Either that or ask someone to bring in a selection of Mills and Boon books, should they exist when you are reading this.

The only details I am prepared to divulge are: it's still amazing and, although no longer a novelty, I can't believe I've been missing out for so many years.

Friday 29 November

9.00 a.m. My birthday! Will be spending most of the day prepping food but I don't care. I'd told the Centre last week I had birthday plans and wouldn't be going in — all true. I was dreading any further questioning on the matter, but luckily they were busy and kept the call brief. It was delicious waking up to a beautiful man, *my* beautiful man! A perfect start to the day.

Saturday 30 November

An unforgettable evening! Fantastic food and my gorgeous friends, all in high spirits, though Sam did have a moment of, 'Will you come back for your birthday next year, Mum?' at which point I filled up but assured her I would, and I most definitely will.

They were all so kind and welcoming towards Lucas. I'm having further pangs of guilt and doubts about leaving them all. I know I'll make new friends and my old faithful ones will always be here, so I shouldn't be negative. Maybe it's due to tiredness and feeling slightly hungover after too much wine. Simon was his usual entertaining self and kept the conversation flowing. Hilary brought her new, invigorated personality along and Sam's Ben made sure Lucas understood the jokes if the conversation was difficult, or too Geordie, to follow! That boy definitely gets my motherly seal of approval. An image popped into my head of a motherly seal — which is exactly how I feel today, having eaten so much last night! I'm incredibly lucky to have these people in my life. Sara, at her wittiest all evening, had us all rolling around with laughter especially when we forced her to tell the Chatty Bob story for those who didn't know it. I love a good raconteur!

They'd clubbed together to buy me the perfect gift: a beautiful photo of the River Tyne and its bridges, silhouetted against a sunset sky; a memoir. As if I'd ever forget that iconic view — never in a million years. Lucas gave me a simple, amethyst bracelet from a craft stall. My style, my favourite colour; carefully chosen with love. Went to bed feeling all gooey and fluffy — yes, in a nice way!

This morning Lucas helped me tidy up then went to see the lawyers for final paperwork. Now it's a matter of days before the recky. Time has suddenly crept up on me, pounced, and now has me pinned firmly to the floor. What's happened? It feels like a week or two at the most since December was months away! Time passes — as my mum used to say, meaning that it marches on with no regard for anyone in its path, singling out those who would rather it slowed down a little.

December

Sunday 1 December — already!

If you were a child in my class you would, at long last, be
allowed to swap Christmas cards, request Christmas songs
and talk about what Santa was bringing you. Up until this
date it was a topic banned from the four walls of the
classroom. Not that it was an easy rule to abide by, when so
many of the shops have had their Christmas stock on
display from September and decorations up since October. I
swear it gets earlier every year — and more annoying. A pub
in town, touting for Christmas party business, had to take its
decorations down in August YES August due to complaints
from customers. I'm looking forward to our last Christmas
here (stomach lurches). Did I write that automatically with
my head, then my heart caught up, causing the lurchy
stomach? Sometimes I get so nervous and anxious at night,
then morning comes and I'm calm and positive again. I
expect it's normal...

Feeling apprehensive about the trip on Wednesday.
Sneaked a look at my diary box when Lucas was out — my
secret haven, my retreat. I may share some of them with
him one day, but not yet. I delved into the box for a lucky
dip, and chose a diary, then a page totally at random. If
you're unlucky enough to get 'School, home, tea (mince) ,
homework, rang Debs' then you're allowed to flick through
a little way in search of something more interesting . Those
are the rules. Needed only a few flicks before finding a
gem: I was fifteen and essentially home alone. Debs had
popped round to make the most of the parents being out,
when the doorbell rang. Under strict instructions *never* to
answer the door without an adult present, we duly ignored
that and rebelliously rushed to answer it. Otherwise, we
might have been in danger of missing out on something,
like David Essex calling to invite us both to a party. Instead,

there on the doorstep stood a large man around forty (ancient), selling cleaning products, tea towels, dishcloths and other equally uninteresting goods. After the initial disappointment of it not being David, we felt sorry for the man, Norman, and in the name of charity and good craic, invited him in thus flying in the face of any personal safety and stranger danger advice.

One whole hour later and still in full flow, demonstrating the entire range of products, it was Norman whose wellbeing was in jeopardy as we were desperate to get rid of him. Seeing the error of our ways and convinced that he had been sent by our parents to teach us a lesson, I could bear the anti-static qualities of the yellow dusters no longer and suddenly shouted out 'RIGHT! We have to go now!' I grabbed the first note I could find from my precious stash of birthday money, snatched a couple of items from him and bundled the nonplussed Norman towards the door saying, 'Take this, it doesn't matter about the change.'

When he'd gone, Debs said, 'Why the hell did you give him twenty quid for two pan scourers and a room spray from the 'Fresh as a Daisy' range? Your mum's going to kill you!'

I'd thought it was five pounds which would have been insane enough, even today, let alone forty years ago! We rushed out of the house and ran frantically up and down the nearby streets, but Norman, who couldn't believe his luck, had well and truly scarpered — and who could blame him? After all, I was stupid enough to give him the money in the first place.

Needless to say, I never told my parents and it took months of milking goats (yes milking goats!) which was my Saturday job, to claw back the birthday money I'd lost, or rather, given away.

I have never bought a room spray since.

Tuesday 3 December

3.00p.m. The estate agent has been. Everything was sparkling and minimalistic — after Sam had been round saying, scornfully, 'Call this decluttered?' and promptly removing the majority of my items like a contestant in *Supermarket Sweep*. It certainly did the trick as the agent said they'd have no problem letting it out — stomach lurched again at that point. It all feels so strange and drastic, having lived here for so long. What if I never come back? I will miss looking out onto my garden and feeling guilty about neglecting it, and I will yearn to be sitting outside in it in the summer. I can't see our London budget stretching to any outside space, and very little indoor space, for that matter!

Had hair coloured and cut for the recky, but now it's a bit too short and I don't feel comfortable about meeting new, younger, and probably trendy London people from South America. Wish I'd had it done last week! Don't know what to take or what to wear. Bag is either too big or too small. Don't know if I should take scruffy or smart-casual. Aaaaargh! Need to sort it now because the train is early and I don't want to be fussing and flapping in front of Lucas. He's never seen me like that.

Wednesday 4 December

London

We're here! Horrendous journey: train packed and underground even worse. At a standstill on the track for half an hour. Joy. Good job Lucas was with me because my bag was ridiculously heavy even though I ditched a load of stuff at the last minute before leaving the house amidst mucho fussing and flapping — to his great amusement. The friends in Elephant and Castle seem pleasant and welcoming, but of course they are all speaking super-fast Spanish and I'm totally lost. The house is incredibly noisy – five people live here sharing two bathrooms. I'm not used to any of this. It's like being a student again. Too old for this lark. Lucas is doing his best to keep my spirits up, bless him.

Had forgotten how many people there are down here. As soon as you step off the train at King's Cross station you ramp up the gears a notch or three and grow a shell of selfishness, leaving your provincial politeness alongside the unread newspaper and dregs of overpriced coffee. The human tidal wave advances and you are forced to battle through it. Deep breath, head down and dive in — it's the only way to survive the journey across the city.

I'm in the room Lucas is staying in until I move down after Christmas. Supposed to be having a nap but I've got a stress headache and travel breath. Must avoid kissing him until that improves. Out later to a salsa club — need to take tablets as we have a busy day viewing flats tomorrow. Excited about that, at least.

Saturday 7 December

On the train home, the 11:50 from King's Cross, in a luxuriously empty carriage. Sad about leaving Lucas but can sum it up thus: peace at last, like the wonderful story by Jill Murphy that I used to read to Sam when she was a little girl.

To say it's been hectic is so much of an understatement that it's practically a lie. It was MANIC! I'm basking in:

a) being on my own

b) not having salsa music blasting out when indoors

c) not breathing in traffic fumes and trying to avoid being flattened when outdoors

Never thought the day would come when I'd regard a train as a welcoming environment, but today it feels like a mini-break of three hours and fifteen glorious minutes.

The first night at the salsa club was fun, I suppose, and although I couldn't talk much, I danced a lot. That said, I felt a bit too stuffy and un-latin in my dancing. I am okay but at a disadvantage not having been weaned on a diet of salsa and merengue — that's not meringue spelt wrongly — it's a type of music! Not being twenty-five with sleek, long black hair and tiny snaky hips doesn't help the cause either. Lucas was great at trying to bolster me up but I still felt old. An old trout out of water.

The house: it got progressively worse. Two of the girls, Clemencia and Lucia, both lovely, friendly young people, brought their boyfriends back to stay so there were then nine people sharing two bathrooms! Had to keep putting the seat down and wiping the floor before standing in some stranger's wee, which is even fouler than a friend's wee. They then had noisy sex and tried to drown it out with equally loud music till about three thirty! Aaaargh! It's exactly like being a student or a twentysomething again — without any of the perks.

Next day I had to force myself up. Lucas seemed oblivious to the noise, laughing it off. He's so grateful for the room and they're giving it to him free for the next few weeks as the previous occupant had paid the rent on it already. He asked, 'Would you rather pay one hundred pounds a night to stay in a hotel?' to which I replied, 'No,' but actually meant, 'YES!'

Trailed around various parts of Southwark viewing one-bed flats which had all looked fine on the internet but were quite blatantly there to deceive: photos taken years ago when first rented out and since then most had been subjected to either a modest earthquake or featured in the programme, *A Life of Grime*. I realised we were going to have to pay a lot more than I bargained for, or live in a studio flat which I can't imagine being good for any relationship. I'm not being materialistic, you understand, merely *real*istic. At least now we have an idea about what we, or rather I, must pay and where we'd not like to live. Lucas will have to take over the flat-hunting as we ran out of time to view any more. It baffles me: here am I, trying to scrub every mark off the wall, touch up the paintwork, get the new-ish carpets cleaned, deep-clean the kitchen and bathroom and these people have the gall to show you around disgusting places with stained carpets, wallpaper peeling off the damp walls, magnanimously saying, 'We could replace the carpet if you want.' No! Replace it first, then show me the flat, and not the one with a load of damp, thank you. But this is London; different rules apply to everything concerning property. Supply and demand. Don't get me started on the selling prices of some of the places we were shown — far too depressing!

I seem to have spent a fortune on … nothing. We went out on only one of the three nights. Nevertheless, travelling around, buying food, entry to a photography exhibition, and a few drinks swallowed up everything I had taken. I had to march myself to a cashpoint to withdraw more. I wasn't being mugged or fined — it just felt like it.

Time to catch up on some sleep.

10.30 p.m. The house feels strange, like a good friend who's been on a massive diet since you last saw them. It looks very different — a bare, sparse, slimmed down version of the one I knew and loved. Your house always looks unfamiliar for a few minutes after a trip away, but this time it really *is* strange as I'm no longer surrounded by my *tat* as Sam calls it, or *clutter* — Simon. I call it my *life*. I purged the place of any unwanted memories when Twat left: nothing bought by him, no photographic evidence. Only a few carefully selected items remained, like my beautiful ceramic hare from the art gallery vouchers I was presented with on my retirement. That hare is not tat. It is not tatty hare! Hope he survives in storage, or rather, Sam's spare room, until I can find a shelf for him in London. A shelf — we'll probably be sleeping on one of those ourselves. There's going to be so little room for anything in the one-bed flat. Still, I'm following my heart, not my head, for once.

Missing Lucas. He's texted saying he's missing me too, but I expect he'll be having good craic in the house with all the music and merriment. I've paid for his train ticket to come back next Sunday but he might be here just for one night, depending on whether he gets offered any work. Also booked one for him for the day before Christmas Eve — all feels a long way off but at the same time I want to enjoy my house while I can and I don't want the time to fly. Sam's invited us for Christmas Day so I don't have the hassle of food shopping, which will be a great help. Having an early night. Something's missing — the cheery brass section of a salsa band ringing in my ears!

Sunday 8 December

Okay, can anyone tell me why this is happening to me now? You wait over a year for a life to come along, then two come at once.

At the Centre, Rob asked if he could talk to me at the end of my afternoon shift. My first reaction was — HE KNOWS! I'm for the chop! Nothing could be further from the truth. Being blissfully ignorant of how unprofessional I really am, he asked if I'd be interested in teaching English to the clients as there's now enough funding for a few hours a week, raised mostly by the Centre. It would be in addition to my regular volunteering day, and he said that it would be excellent if I could commit to it. I can't quite believe this. Not only do I feel dreadful about the pretence I have to put up regarding Lucas, I now have to lie and say that I'll think about it, when I know I'm going to be gone in a few weeks' time! This tangled web is beginning to strangle me. Will have to put the conversation out of my mind or it will consume every last morsel of me. It would have been perfect for me this time last year to have had an offer like that. Must move forward and not look back. I've never been a 'what if?' type and I'm not going to start now!

Monday 9 December

Spoke to Lucas about a flat in Borough he viewed. It sounded foul — even looked dark and dingy on the website. Although in the higher price range we're forced to go up to, it was nonetheless miniscule and unimpressive. He said it was 'okay' in the voice of someone trying to make the best of a bad job and put on a front. After further interrogation I gave it the thumbs down and told him to keep looking. He said Elephant and Castle is cheaper so he'll go back there and resume the search.

It's all very difficult. The rent I can ask for my lovely house here will not be sufficient to pay for the privilege of living in a teeny weeny London hovel. Such is life. 'Get over it!' Sara will tell me, 'Everything has its price.' She means love, Lucas, and happiness — hopefully. I've opened wine and already feel like I've had too much.

Tuesday 10 December

Very low today. Assume it's because I'm hungover. Rang around the salsa clubs and anywhere that runs classes in the vain hope of finding enough work to keep Lucas up here in Newcastle.

I ran into Simon in town this afternoon and we went to the Christmas market. It looked so beautiful with its festive lights, seasonal food smells from all corners of Europe complementing the atmosphere perfectly. Simon loved my story about the Dutch flower stall at the same market last year. I was there browsing on a weekday when Santa's little helper — a fully grown man in an elf costume, said, in a sinister tone, 'Do you want to see Santa?' I replied that I was far too scared, and scurried away, giggling. I remember how it cheered me up no end on a depressing December day.

We sampled gluhwein from Germany, mulled wine from England, more wine from Italy and gorged on mince pies, cheese and cakes from every other EU country! Afterwards, we had an impromptu pub crawl instigated by him, naturally. It was brilliant! I adore spontaneity — went in search of a couple of storage boxes but came back with half the Christmas import quota for the European Union bursting out of my bag-for-life! I have no recollection of buying the hand-made felt St Nicholas tree decoration, the pair of miniature Christmas clogs or the reindeer fashioned out of a cork. As for the nativity scene whittled from Scandinavian Spruce, whatever possessed me? We pondered the fate of the Christmas market post-Brexit. It would be tragic if it were scrapped and were plunged back into the dark ages when pizza was considered exotic in Britain.

Felt worse later and had to have a sleep. What if I want to do that in London and it's too noisy? I'll have to buy earplugs as well as storage boxes on my second attempt and must avoid the market!

Friday 13 December

Nothing bad happened today so don't ever believe in superstitious nonsense or you are wasting your life. There are far more important things to worry about — I know.

My feet have hardly touched the ground during these past few days. Been out with Sara and Simon, round to Hilary's who's at a slightly irritating stage in her new relationship whereby that's all she wants talk about. Must remind myself of what she used to be like: similar i.e. me, me, me, but all boring and negative so I should be grateful. Actually, it was lovely looking out onto the river from her flat with the twinkling lights from the city, wondering how much it would cost to rent a similar place in London! Can't bear to think about all that and, although I am missing Lucas, I've been on a constant socialising binge. I'm telling myself it's because I'm leaving soon, and it's Christmas when everywhere is atmospheric and even the dingiest place looks pretty, that it isn't the norm.

Bought a small artificial Christmas tree. A real one would have been a hassle to dispose of and clean up after we leave. To make things even more difficult, the house is looking beautiful — as well as tidy. I'm feeling very sad about leaving it. As for leaving Sam and my lovely friends, I can't imagine what an emotional wreck I will be.

Saturday 14 December

A very mixed day indeed. Agent rang — next week some people are coming to view the house. I was starting to worry about it as I certainly can't afford to pay a London rent out of my pension and what little's left out of the divorce settlement. Despite all that economically sensible head stuff, I put the phone down with a horrendous sinking feeling in the pit of my stomach, as if it were signalling 'this is it'. Must ignore it. Lucas will be back tomorrow.

Sam called by and admired the decorations. There were tears in her eyes when she left, and I managed to close the door with a millisecond to spare before my own floodgates opened and cried for what seemed like hours. The cork reindeer ended up somewhat on the damp side as I clutched it in a melodramatic fashion a la Scarlett O'Hara in *Gone with the Wind*. I may be joking about it but actually I'm feeling terribly sad. Will hopefully cheer up for Lucas.

Sunday 15 December

Had a relaxing morning doing very little. Lucas arrived around one o'clock — very animated having been working again, feeling valued and contributing to society after so long being prevented from doing so. Although he's always remained incredibly cheerful throughout the entire asylum seeking process with the barrage of stress and angst that it brings, he now has a positive glow about him; his eyes are bright, youthful, beautiful. We went into town and he loved the Christmas lights. Took him to see Fenwick's window — a must for all Newcastle children! The department store puts on a spectacular, elaborate display spanning five or six windows with moving, mechanical figures in each one. Children and adults alike queue all the way down Northumberland Street to admire it; a Geordie tradition. We perused the Christmas market, sensibly avoiding the alcohol (boring).

Newcastle United were playing at home. Football: the official religion of the North East. Place of worship: St James' Park — a towering, imposing structure, visible not only from space, but also from most parts of the city. Twat was unattractively snobbish about football, preferring rugby. I, on the other hand, hate rugby and have always enjoyed following the ups and frequent downs of my home team. We watched the loyal supporters, the 'Toon Army' — a snaking mass of black and white stripes, men and women engrossed in the serious business of team-talk, marching into battle at the stadium. Once inside, supporters from the visiting team may be spotted in the distance, banished to the uppermost corner, where the air is thin and oxygen is in short supply.

Envious of the profound sense of belonging I knew they'd be experiencing, I told Lucas about my early dalliance with football. As covertly rebellious teenagers, Chris and I used to sneak out regularly to watch the matches, black and white scarves and hats secreted in our bags, claiming we were off into town to buy records and make-up. The football ground in the seventies was deemed much too dangerous a place for fifteen-year-old girls who were determined to stand on the terraces in the Leazes end. It entailed shoving, shouting, singing, swearing, and avoiding wee, in equal amounts. With the exception of the wee avoidance, we found the whole experience exhilarating and revelled in being a part of it, unbeknown to our parents.

I regret not having returned to St James' Park since then! I ought to have gone this year when I was searching for new interests. Perhaps Hilary would have come with me. Now it's too late. Really must hide the diary well tonight!

We came back and had pizza and wine in front of the coal effect fire, which is more romantic than it sounds, I can assure you.

I'm going through a period of extremes: highs followed by lows. Not sure what to expect next.

Monday 16 December

Ran into Minika this morning when we were going to the local shop. She was very excited to see Lucas again so we took her for a coffee and a catch-up. Luckily, neither Rob, Ken nor the other volunteers live nearby so we have managed to avoid them so far. It would be extremely annoying to be discovered a couple of weeks before we leave! Lucas insisted on catching the overnight coach back as he's teaching tomorrow and it's considerably cheaper. Asked him if all the women in the salsa class love him — I'm a tad jealous because I know anyone over forty is bound to fancy him. He gave me the right answers: 'I doubt it, I wouldn't know and I wouldn't care if they did. You're the one for me,' etcetera. Full marks!

He's gone now. Feeling sad but strangely calm and not in the least bit lonely. I counted down the days — there aren't many left until Christmas. Then I'll be leaving.

Tuesday 17 December

What's wrong with me? I've done a stupid, stupid thing! The estate agents brought a young couple to see the house so I made myself scarce. He's an engineer and she, ironically, will be working in an estate agents' office in town. They're moving up from Manchester for his work. Agent rang last thing this afternoon saying that he had great news, they want the house, adding, 'Although, they don't like the shower over the bath and think the kitchen is dated.'

What? My little pride and, now sparkling, joy? My gorgeous kitchen where I spend ages staring out of the window at the birds and fretting about the state of the garden? What a bloody cheek! So — I told him they couldn't have it. Yes, I've withdrawn it, from them anyway. How dare they! My kitchen is retro, *not* dated. Well I suppose the difference is in the terminology but I don't care. It's still damn rude. I don't think I'll tell Lucas. God, a relationship kicking off with secrets and deceit. That's a good start. What have I done?! Maybe I'll ring them back tomorrow and apologise. No. They're not having it. If it's not good enough for them then *they're* definitely not good enough for *it*. That's that, I think.

Wednesday 18 December

Slept badly. Head's spinning. Thinking all night about those nasty people. How could they say such things? Rang Sam who was very shirty at first and said, 'Are you a mentalist?' and, 'Don't you want to rent the flaming house out? Who else do you think's going to come along the week before Christmas looking for a house?' Then, after hearing the silence from her crazy mother at the other end she said, softly, 'I'll come over after work.'

10.30 p.m. Sam's only just left, bless her little heart. She said that although I was being far too sensitive she could see my point and maybe someone else will come along next week and make no criticism of the place and it'll all work out in the end. I reassured her that yes, I would be fine with that. All I ask is for someone to love the house and cherish it for me while I'm away — for how long? If the plan is to sell up eventually — oh God, the thought makes me shudder — then I won't be returning therefore shouldn't be so concerned. What will happen after that? Need to stop this nonsense, nip it in the bud. It's Christmas at the end of next week and time's running out for prospective tenants for January. I've been rash and irresponsible.

Thursday 19 December

Not a good day.
Slept badly, again. Told Lucas about refusing to have the Manchester people. Was so worried about his reaction. At first he was silent then asked me THE question, kindly, calmly, gently, like the placid, thoughtful soul that he is, 'Lizzie, are you sure you want to come to London?' Mustering up a positive voice of conviction I replied, 'Yes of course I do!' and other platitudes like, 'It'll be fine. Someone else will want the house and even if they say they hate it with a passion I will gladly go ahead and rent it to them,' followed by forced laughter.

Came off the phone and cried, again. Had two glasses of wine and went to bed, worrying about trivia such as when will I find the time or motivation to do some Christmas shopping — ridiculous!

2.00 a.m. Can't sleep. Head's whirring round and round, heart's pounding. WHAT AM I DOING? I don't want to leave. I love him but I don't want to leave. I absolutely do not want to leave my daughter, my home, my friends, the Centre, my potential new job and a new life I'm finally enjoying. But how can I possibly back out now? What would I say to Lucas? Had my chance today, a perfect opportunity offered on a plate and I chickened out. I'm pathetic. Calm down! It's night time collywobbles as Mum would say. I wish she were here. It'll all look different in the morning. I'll be fine. Deep breaths.

Friday 20 December

9.30 a.m. Black-eye Friday. The last Friday before Christmas when people have too much to drink and end up fighting. There will be no fighting here, but there may be anger when I drop this bombshell on poor Lucas, especially after reassuring him that everything is fine.

I'm not going. I can't leave. There I've said it and it feels so right but so dreadfully wrong at the same time. He's going to be devastated. How on earth am I going to tell him? He'll hate me. He might want nothing more to do with me and I will have to respect that. I'll miss him. Can I live without him? What about January when the Christmas sparkle has been well and truly extinguished, the Scandinavian Spruce packed away, and the daily grind once again kicks in? I'll have my new job at the Centre, teaching English — I would love to do that! I saw an Art History course advertised at the University too — that'd be ideal. I'm ready. I'm better — apart from feeling sick at the thought of telling Lucas, that is. What if I miss him too much, want to move down there with him then he doesn't want to bother with me in case I change my mind again… aaagh! Too many ifs. What I do know for sure is that I feel a tidal wave of relief sweeping over me. It knocked my feet from under me, but not for long; I'm back up and the suffocating dread of leaving has gone. I can breathe. I have a life to look forward to — either with Lucas or without him, I can cope. Must ring Sam!

11.00 p.m. Sam cried on the phone. She has always been the stoical, no-nonsense type, not prone to waterworks. Takes after her father, not me. But she cried, tears of joy. I knew I'd made the right choice. Instead of making another right choice and ringing Lucas, I chose to bury my wretched, gutless head in the sand, or rather, my diaries — my comfort blankets, my solace. Regardless of the fact that he could be trailing around London as we speak, pointlessly viewing flats, I chose to keep him in the dark for another night and tell him in the morning.

I found the sixth form Christmas disco entry where I 'got off with' Ian, a guy I'd fancied for a while — the perfect Christmas gift! Spent the next week snogging him beside the lockers during breaks, lunchtimes and in every free lesson we had together. Debs was most annoyed by the end of the term and said I'd need new lips from Santa as mine must be worn down to the bone! Yuk! I laughed and laughed, enjoying the brief respite from reality but as soon as I thought about poor Lucas, normal stomach-churning service was resumed. I'm dreading tomorrow, but beneath the fear is a voice. I know I sound like the crazy woman again but it's true, it's the voice of calm, the voice that says, 'Don't worry, you know you're doing the right thing. It'll be fine.' Mum's voice.

Saturday 21 December

It felt like I was leaving him, finishing the relationship for good, which, although it's not what I want, I have to accept that he might choose not to continue a long distance arrangement. Cried buckets after the call. He was unbelievably lovely. I'd scarcely managed to force one word out, 'Lucas,' when he finished the sentence, 'You're not coming to London.' I'm the luckiest woman alive. He was so understanding and said that after he'd asked me the question the other day, he could tell by my tone of voice that I wasn't happy. He knew. He's such a sensitive man and, unlike many in that situation, so selfless. 'I knew how you were feeling. You love your home, family and friends too much. You belong there, Lizzie, and I want you to be happy.' I broke down on the phone. Told him it isn't his fault and that I love him and still want him. I think he knows. Then I had the massive cry and opened some wine. Cried some more and came to bed clutching one of his few possessions, a tee shirt he'd left behind. I buried my head in it, breathing in his delicious smell.

I will miss this man so much.

Sunday 22 December

So, you lovely Shady Pines residents and other diary readers, whoever you may be: if your memory serves you well, you will have been chuckling along throughout my days of wondering what was going to happen in the end. So, I didn't go skipping off to London like a twentysomething after all. I have to face reality, waking up in the cold light of a December day I can't expect to have it all ways. Lucas may well choose to finish the relationship — and who could blame him? I must prepare myself for that possibility. He's supposed to be coming up tomorrow, for Christmas. I didn't dare ask yesterday if he still intends to come. I'll suffer the consequences of my actions when I start wishing he was here, instead of being alone again. Will have to keep busy and remind myself that I could be sharing a house with five noisy young people instead, as the last-minute flat-hunting proved unsuccessful. That was a relief! I could have handed over two thousand pounds or more and been locked into a rental contract for a year had we been less choosy about where we wanted to rent. A narrow escape if ever there was one.

Spent all morning ringing round friends, leaving voicemails and sending texts. Hours of life-affirming conversations. I love my friends with a passion. They were all concerned about Lucas but reassured me that he'll be fine there with his work and ready-made community. I'm beginning to accept that, unlike me, he is someone who will thrive anywhere and rise to the challenge. They're right, he needs to work. Again, I bottled out of asking if he was coming up, although I'd sent him the train tickets. Simply texted to say that I'm sorry and I love him. He replied, magnanimous as ever, 'You have to follow your soul,' which made me cry all over again. He's right. The soul lies even deeper than the heart. Mine belongs here.

Monday 23 December

When people say that they've been through the wringer, I now know exactly what they mean. Though I'm drained, I have come through it feeling surprisingly calm in the knowledge that I've made the right decision, which rarely happens to me.

Lucas texted to say he was coming up today as planned, unless I thought it best that he didn't , but had booked a coach ticket to go back this evening. Of course I urged him to come, even for that short amount of time — it's better than the highly likely prospect of never seeing him again. He's already had invitations for Christmas from his London friends and he thought it best not to get too comfortable together for two weeks as it would be terribly difficult to part, come the new year. Miles more sensible than I am.

A rocky roller coaster of a day. Spent a small part of it in bed. Maybe not the best idea but couldn't help myself — feels like a new box of forbidden chocolates has been opened; they could be my last ever treat. Kept doubting myself, feeling desperately sad, looking at his beautiful, serene face but the eyes have lost some of their previous sparkle. That's my fault. He is young. He will survive, something our relationship would not do if I went to London with feelings of resentment. I'd be lonely, trapped in the evenings in a tiny rented apartment while he is out working. I may be able to teach the odd class or volunteer at a refugee centre, but it takes a long time to make friends when you have no regular workplace. My friends who used to live in London have all moved right out, away from the centre and miles from Southwark.

Why he doesn't hate me, I can't imagine. Some men would be furious, allowing their own selfish pride to take over any feelings they had for the other person and focus on how they were going to face their new friends, having been effectively dumped; the chuckee, not the chucker. It gets worse — to avoid a long, agonising goodbye, he insisted on walking to the station himself. As he left, he pressed a small box into my hand. Inside was a silver chain and hanging from it, an exquisite, simple, glass heart. On a carefully folded note, he had written, 'Thank you for saving me. All my love, L.' Yet more torrents of tears.

Now I'm okay, content. I need to let go and let him move on. A long distance relationship like this one won't work. I am, thankfully, old enough to know that for sure. A list is called for.

Things to look forward to:

- Christmas with Sam and the gang — she's also invited Minika.
- New job at the Centre — must ring them to accept!
- Not having to lie when at the Centre.
- Art History class — must email to enrol!
- A clean, tidy, decluttered house.
- Football with Hilary?
- Possibly seeing Lucas in the new year.
- A whole new life.

Reasons to be miserable:

- I will miss Lucas — I can handle it.

Christmas Eve Tuesday 24 December

Can't wait for tomorrow! I've made another positive decision: after Christmas I'll ask the doctor to begin the process of reducing the antidepressants. They've served me well but I'm fairly confident I can go it alone now, with a little help from my fantastic friends.

Scouted through diaries for Christmas — the party season for students. Found a great one: another fancy dress do — yes, more humiliation!

Had to ring Debs to tell her all about my new life plan and also to read out the diary entry of the student fancy dress party we were invited to in Jesmond, when I went as a bunch of grapes. It took hours to blow up and carefully attach green balloons to my body-stocking and the whole thing looked most effective. The evening began promisingly and I went with Steve, a guy I was casually seeing at the time. However, by the time Debs and the others arrived (which wasn't much later) every single one of the balloons had been maliciously popped and I spent the rest of the very long night feeling totally exposed in my green tights and brown body-stocking with now limp pieces of rubber dangling pathetically from it! Having had endless sneering, quizzical looks from the cool people dressed as gorgeous flapper girls from *The Great Gatsby*, Catwomen and the like, I resorted to sticking a note on my back which said, 'When I left the house I was a bunch of grapes.' I obviously didn't think it through! Debs and I laughed till we couldn't breathe on the phone and the tears streamed down my face. It was the perfect tonic! Must ask Sam to buy me a new diary for Christmas, she keeps asking for ideas.

Met Sara for an early pizza — it was noisy with a few parties in full flow, but they added to the atmosphere. She drank too much wine before she ate and was very funny; kept telling me over and over how happy she was now that I'm not leaving after all. I feel loved and exceptionally privileged to have such fabulous friends. At one point Sara leaned over and announced, 'Look at you now, Lizzie Moffitt, you're a new woman!' Tipsy or not, she was right; I've journeyed far and I am happy. So, new year, new life, whatever you have in store for me, bring it on — I'm ready for you!

About The Author

Maya George was born in Newcastle upon Tyne where she now lives with her husband. She has travelled extensively, living and working in London, Mallorca, and Colombia. Throughout her life, Maya has continually campaigned against all forms of injustice and inequality. She loves life, her job, people, animals, and her home city.

email: mayageorge18@yahoo.com